Traditional Russian
Fairy Tales
reflected in lacquer
miniatures

Яркий город

Yarky Gorod Art Publishers
2016

*In 2009 Kholui lacquer miniature painting is celebrating
a major anniversary – 75 years from the foundation
of the cooperative that developed into the most important
local enterprise and produced many talented artists.*

Artist Nina Babarkina
Translated from the Russian by Paul Williams
Photographer Alexander Rodionov
Design Inna Zezegova
Editor Natalia Morozova
Type-setting Nina Sokolova
Colour correction Tatiana Chernyshenko
Technical director Peter Krakovsky

*The publishers thank Dmitry Kuznetsov
for his assistance in the making of this book.*

ISBN 978-5-9663-0143-9

Contents

At the Pike's Behest

There was once an old man who had three sons. Two of them were bright fellows; the third, called Yemélia, was a bit of a fool. While his brothers worked, Yemelia spent his days lying on the stove and took no interest in anything.

One day Yemelia's two brothers had gone to the market, and their wives decided to send him for water.

"Fetch some water, Yemelia."

But he called down from the stove:

"I don't feel like it."

"Fetch some water, or you won't get anything tasty when your brothers come back from market."

"Oh, all right then."

Yemelia climbed down off the stove, pulled on his coat and boots, took a couple of buckets and an axe and went down to the stream. He broke a hole in the ice, filled the buckets and put them on the bank. He looked into the hole in the ice and spotted a pike in the water. He dropped down and somehow managed to catch hold of the pike and pull it out.

"This will make fine fish soup!"

Suddenly the pike spoke to him in a human voice:

"Yemelia, put me back in the water. I shall be of use to you."

Yemelia just laughed:

"Now how can you be of use to me? No, I'll take you home and my brothers' wives can turn you into soup. You'll make fine soup."

The pike begged him again:

"Yemelia, o Yemelia. Put me back in the water and I shall do everything you ask."

"Very well, but first prove that you're not deceiving me, then I'll let you go."

The pike replied:

"Yemelia, tell me what you want just now."

"I want... I want the buckets to take themselves home, and not spill a drop of water."

The pike replied:

"Remember these words, and when you want something just say:

      'At my request,

      At the pike's behest.'"

Yemelia repeated after him:

      "At my request,

      At the pike's behest —

      buckets, take yourselves off home."

As soon as he had spoken, the buckets stirred and headed back up the slope. Yemelia slid the pike back into the water and followed the buckets.

The buckets passed through the village and everyone who was about stopped and stared. Yemelia walked behind grinning. The buckets went into the house and set themselves down on the bench, while Yemelia climbed back onto the stove.

After a time, his sisters-in-law called out:
"Yemelia, why are you lying down? Go and chop some firewood."
"I don't feel like it."
"Chop some firewood, or you won't get anything tasty when your brothers come back from market."

Yemelia climbed unwillingly down from the stove. Then he remembered about the pike and quietly said:

"At my request,
At the pike's behest —
go, axe, and chop wood,
and firewood come into the house
and stack yourself by the stove."

The axe sprang up from under the bench, flew out into the yard and chopped the wood in the blinking of an eye. The chopped wood came

inside and stacked itself by the stove.

After a time, Yemelia's sisters-in-law called out:

"Yemelia, we've run right out of wood. Go into the forest and cut some."

But he called down from the stove:

"What are you here for?"

"What do you mean? It's not our job to go into the forest for wood!"

"I don't feel like it."

"Well then, you won't get anything tasty."

There was nothing for it. Yemelia climbed down off the stove, pulled on his coat and boots, took a rope and an axe. He went out into the yard and sat in the sledge.

"Hey, you, women! Open the gate!"

His sisters-in-law shouted:

"Why are you sitting in the sledge, you fool, when you haven't harnessed up the horse?"

"I don't need a horse!"

The women opened the gate, and Yemelia quietly said:

> "At my request,
> At the pike's behest —
> sledge, carry me to the forest."

The sledge stirred and sped out of the gate so fast that a horseman would have been left behind.

To get to the forest, though, Yemelia had to go through the town and he knocked down quite a few people who failed to get out of the way in time. The townsfolk shouted, "Catch him! Stop him!" but Yemelia urged his sledge on even faster. He came to the forest:

> "At my request,
> At the pike's behest —
> axe, cut down firewood,
> as dry as you can find.
> Firewood tie yourself in bundles
> and stack yourself in the sledge."

Then Yemelia had the axe cut him a cudgel so big and heavy he could hardly lift it. He got back on the sledge and:

> "At my request,
> At the pike's behest —
> sledge, carry me back home."

The sledge started back.

Again Yemelia had to go through the town where he had knocked people down, but this time they were expecting him. The men seized Yemelia and dragged him from the sledge. They beat and cursed him. Yemelia saw he was in real trouble and quietly said:

> "At my request,
> At the pike's behest —
> up, cudgel, and give them a thrashing."

The heavy cudgel sprang up and battered the men until they fled. Ivan drove home and climbed back onto the stove. In time the Tsar himself came to hear of Yemelia's deeds and he sent one of his officers to find him and bring him to the palace.

The officer drove into the village, came into the house where Yemelia lived and asked:

"Are you Yemelia the Fool?"

"What's it to you?" came the voice from the stove.

"Get dressed quickly. I am to take you to the Tsar."

"I don't feel like it."

At that the officer lost his temper and slapped Yemelia on the cheek.
And Yemelia quietly said:

> "At my request,
> At the pike's behest —
> up, cudgel, and give him a thrashing."

The heavy cudgel sprang up and battered the officer, who barely managed to get away. The Tsar was surprised that his officer had not managed to deal with Yemelia and called his grandest courtier:

"Fetch Yemelia the Fool here to the palace, or else I'll have your head from your shoulders."

The grandest courtier bought raisins, prunes and spice-cakes and went off to the village. He went into the house and there he asked the women what Yemelia liked.

"Our Yemelia likes it when people ask him kindly and promise him a fine outfit — then he'll do whatever you ask."

The grandest courtier gave Yemelia the raisins, prunes and spice-cakes and said:

"Yemelia, my boy, why are you lying here on the stove? Let's go and see the Tsar."

"I'm warm enough where I am."

"Yemelia, my boy, there'll be good things to eat and drink at the palace. Come on, let's go."

"I don't feel like it."

"Yemelia, my boy, the Tsar will give you a fine caftan, and a hat and boots."

Yemelia thought and thought.

"Very well. You go on ahead, and I shall be right behind you."

The grandest courtier drove off, but Yemelia stayed lying down and just said:

> "At my request,
> At the pike's behest —
> stove, carry me to the Tsar."

At that the joints between the logs of the house sprang apart, the roof shook, one wall fell away and the stove lumbered out into the street and off down the road, straight to the palace.

The Tsar happened to look out of the window and was astonished:

"What's this wonder?"

The greatest courtier replied:

"That's Yemelia coming to see you on his stove."

The Tsar went out onto the porch:

"Well, Yemelia, I've heard a lot of complaints against you. You've knocked down a lot of people."

"Why did they get in front of my sledge?"

At that moment the Tsar's daughter, Princess Maria, looked out of the window. Yemelia saw her in the window and said quietly:

> "At my request,
> At the pike's behest —
> make the Tsar's daughter fall in love with me."

Then he added:

> "And, stove, carry me home."

The stove turned around and went back home. It entered the house and settled back in its place. Yemelia carried on lying there as before. Meanwhile the Tsar's palace was full of sighs and tears. Princess Maria was pining for Yemelia. She said she could not live without him and begged her father to let her marry him. Greatly disturbed and irritated, the Tsar called his grandest courtier once again:

"Go and fetch Yemelia here, alive or dead, or else I'll have your head from your shoulders.

The grandest courtier bought sweet wines and different delicacies and went off to the village. He went into the house and regaled Yemelia with all of them. Yemelia ate and drank his fill, then turned over and fell fast asleep. The grandest courtier carried him out to his carriage and drove him to the palace. The Tsar immediately ordered his men to bring a large barrel with iron hoops. They placed Yemelia and Princess Maria inside, sealed the barrel up and tossed it into the sea. Eventually the buffeting woke Yemelia up. He found himself somewhere dark and cramped and groaned:

"Where on earth am I?"

"Alas, dear Yemelia," a voice answered, "we have been sealed up in a barrel and thrown into the sea."

"And who are you?"

"I am Princess Maria."

Then Yemelia said:

> "At my request,
> At the pike's behest —
> strong winds, drive this barrel to shore,
> onto the yellow sands."

The strong winds blew. The sea rose and tossed the barrel out onto the shore, onto the yellow sands. Yemelia and the Princess climbed out.

"Dear Yemelia, where shall we live? Build us some kind of a hut."

"I don't feel like it."

The Princess begged him to do it, and he said:

> "At my request,
> At the pike's behest —
> build me a palace of stone with a roof of gold."

No sooner had he spoken, than a palace of stone appeared with a roof of gold. All around it was a green garden full of flowers blooming and birds singing.

Princess Maria and Yemelia went inside and sat by one of the windows.

"Dear Yemelia, couldn't you become handsome?"

Yemelia did not stop long to think:

> "At my request,
> At the pike's behest —
> turn me into a fine figure of a man,
> a sight for sore eyes."

And Yemelia became fairer in face and body than can be imagined or described. Just then the Tsar was out hunting. when he noticed a palace standing where there had been nothing before.

"Who has dared to build a palace on my land without my permission?"

And he sent some of his courtiers to find out.

The messengers rode into the garden and called up to the window.

Yemelia leaned out and said:

"Ask the Tsar to come and be my guest. I shall tell him everything myself."

The Tsar accepted the invitation. Yemelia met him, conducted him into the palace and brought him to the dining-room. They sat down to a feast. The Tsar ate and drank, marvelling all the time:

"But who are you, my fine young sir?"

"You remember Yemelia the Fool who came to see you on a stove and you had him and your daughter sealed up in a barrel and thrown into the sea. I am that same Yemelia. If the fancy takes me, I can burn and ruin your whole kingdom."

The Tsar was terrified at that and began begging forgiveness:

"Marry my daughter, dear Yemelia. Take my kingdom, only spare me!"

There was a great feast to which everyone was invited. Yemelia married Princess Maria and began to rule the kingdom.

Now the tale has all been told; if you listened well, you're as good as gold.

Sister Alionushka
and Brother Ivanushka

Once upon a time there were an old man and woman who had a daughter named Aliónushka and a young son named Ivánushka. The old couple died and Alionushka and Ivanushka were left alone, without anybody in the whole wide world. Alionushka went out to work and took her brother with her. They walked a long way through the fields and Ivanushka grew thirsty.

"Sister Alionushka, I want to drink!"

"Wait, little brother, until we get to the well."

They walked and walked. The sun stood high in the sky; the well was still far off, and the heat was stifling. They came to a cattle trough full of water.

"Sister Alionushka, let me take a sip from the trough!"

"Don't drink, little brother, or you'll turn into a calf."

Ivanushka obeyed her and they walked on.

The sun stood high in the sky; the well was still far off, and the heat was stifling. They came to a horse trough full of water.

"Sister Alionushka, let me take a sip from the trough!"

"Don't drink, little brother, or you'll turn into a foal."

Ivanushka sighed, and they walked on again.

They walked and walked. The sun stood high in the sky; the well was still far off, and the heat was stifling. They came to a goat trough full of water.

Ivanushka said:

"Sister Alionushka, I can't go on: I must drink from this trough!"

"Don't drink, little brother, or you'll turn into a kid."

Ivanushka did not heed her and drank his fill from the trough.

He slaked his thirst and ... turned into a kid!

Alionushka called to her brother, but instead of Ivanushka a little white goat came running after her. Alionushka burst into tears. She sat down under a haystack to cry, while the kid gambolled around her.

Just then a merchant drove by in his cart.

"Why are you crying, beautiful maiden?"

Alionushka told him her of her misfortune.

The merchant said:

"Well, why don't you marry me. I'll dress you in gold and silver, and the little goat will live with us."

Alionushka thought and thought and agreed to marry the merchant.

She moved into his house and they all lived together. The goat ate and drank with them. Once, when the merchant was away, a witch appeared from out of nowhere. She stood under Alionushka's window and called her to come and bathe in the river. She was so persuasive that Alionushka did go down to the river with her. When they got there, the witch seized Alionushka, fastened a stone round her neck and threw her into the water. Then the witch made herself the very image of Alionushka, dressed in her clothes and went into her house. Nobody noticed the change. Even the merchant

when he came back believed that she was Alionushka. Only the little goat knew the truth. He pined away, refusing to eat or drink. Morning and evening he went down to the river bank and called out:

"Alionushka, sister dear,
Come out of the river and back to me here."

The witch found out and began asking her husband to slaughter the kid.

The merchant felt sorry for the little goat as he had grown very fond of him, but the witch nagged so much that at last he agreed. The witch commanded the servants to build fires in the yard, to heat the iron caldrons and to sharpen the knives.

The goat realised that he had not long to live and said to his foster-father:

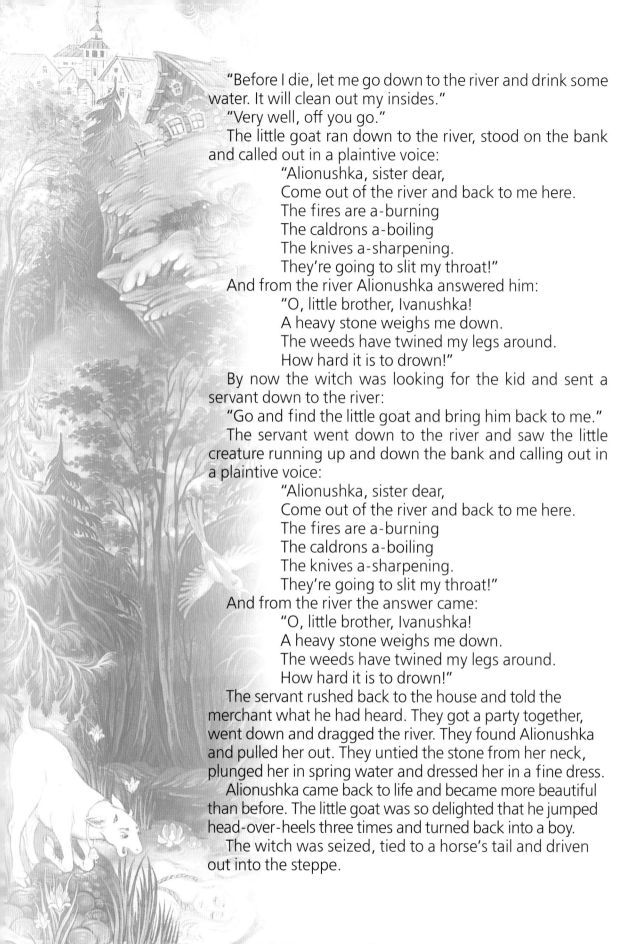

"Before I die, let me go down to the river and drink some water. It will clean out my insides."

"Very well, off you go."

The little goat ran down to the river, stood on the bank and called out in a plaintive voice:

"Alionushka, sister dear,
Come out of the river and back to me here.
The fires are a-burning
The caldrons a-boiling
The knives a-sharpening.
They're going to slit my throat!"

And from the river Alionushka answered him:

"O, little brother, Ivanushka!
A heavy stone weighs me down.
The weeds have twined my legs around.
How hard it is to drown!"

By now the witch was looking for the kid and sent a servant down to the river:

"Go and find the little goat and bring him back to me."

The servant went down to the river and saw the little creature running up and down the bank and calling out in a plaintive voice:

"Alionushka, sister dear,
Come out of the river and back to me here.
The fires are a-burning
The caldrons a-boiling
The knives a-sharpening.
They're going to slit my throat!"

And from the river the answer came:

"O, little brother, Ivanushka!
A heavy stone weighs me down.
The weeds have twined my legs around.
How hard it is to drown!"

The servant rushed back to the house and told the merchant what he had heard. They got a party together, went down and dragged the river. They found Alionushka and pulled her out. They untied the stone from her neck, plunged her in spring water and dressed her in a fine dress.

Alionushka came back to life and became more beautiful than before. The little goat was so delighted that he jumped head-over-heels three times and turned back into a boy.

The witch was seized, tied to a horse's tail and driven out into the steppe.

Morozko

Once upon a time there was a peasant who lived with his second wife. Each had one daughter from their first marriages. Everyone knows what it can be like to live with a step-mother: do something too much and you are beaten, don't do it enough and you are beaten. Yet her own daughter, whatever she does, gets patted on the head and praised to the skies. The step-daughter fed and watered the animals, brought firewood and water into the kitchen, stoked the stove and swept out the house — all before it was even light. Yet nothing pleased the woman — everything was done wrong. The wind might howl for a time, but then it falls silent, while an old woman when she gets worked up can just go on and on. The step-mother eventually decided to be rid of the girl altogether.

"Take her out in the sledge," she told her husband, "wherever you want, so that she is out of my sight forever! Take her to the forest and leave her in the freezing cold!"

The old man was grief-stricken and his eyes filled with tears, but his wife nagged so much he had to agree. He harnessed the horse to the sledge and said:

"Come, daughter dear, and ride in the sledge."

He took the unfortunate girl into the forest, tipped her into a snow-drift beneath a huge fir-tree and hurried away. The girl sat beneath the fir and shivered. Soon she was shaking from head to foot. Suddenly she heard Morózko — which is what the Russians call Jack Frost — nearby, making his way through the firs, leaping from tree to tree, snapping and cracking as he went. He sprang onto the top of the fir, below which the girl was sitting, and called down to her:

"Are you warm, my girl?"

"Quite warm, dear Morozko, quite warm."

Morozko started to come down the tree and the snapping and cracking grew stronger:

"Are you warm, my girl?

Are you warm, my beauty?"

"Quite warm, dear Morozko, quite warm."

She could hardly get the words out.

Morozko came lower still, snapping and cracking all the more:

"Are you warm, my girl?

Are you warm, my beauty?

Are you warm, my sweet?"

The girl was frozen to the bone. She could barely move her tongue:

"Oh, quite warm, Morozko, my darling!"

At that Morozko took pity on the girl, wrapped her snugly in furs, and warmed her with quilted blankets. Meanwhile the step-mother was preparing for her wake, cooking pancakes, as is the Russian tradition. She called out to her husband:

"Go on then, you old fool, bring your daughter back for burial!"

The old man went off to the forest and when he got to the spot where he had left her he found his daughter sitting there ruddy-cheeked and happy. She was wearing a sable coat and gold and silver from head to foot, while a chest of rich presents lay next to her. The old man was overjoyed, loaded everything into the sledge, sat his daughter alongside him and headed for home.

Meanwhile the old woman was still cooking pancakes, when from under the table the dog barked out:

     "Woof, woof!
     The old man's daughter will come in silver and gold;
     the old woman's daughter will leave suitors cold."

The woman tossed him a pancake:

     "Those are the wrong words. You should say:
     'The old woman's daughter will soon be wed;
     the old man's daughter is dead, dead, dead.'"

The dog ate the pancake and repeated:

     "Woof, woof!
     The old man's daughter will come in silver and gold;
     the old woman's daughter will leave suitors cold."

The old woman tried giving him pancakes and tried beating him, but the dog would not change his tune... Suddenly the gates creaked, the door flew open and in came her step-

daughter, decked in gold and silver, looking simply radiant. Behind her the old man carried the large, heavy chest. The old woman stared and threw up her arms...

"Quick, you old fool, harness the other horse to the sledge! Take my daughter into the forest and leave her in the same place."

The man put his wife's daughter in the sledge, took her into the forest, tipped her into the same snow-drift beneath the huge fir and hurried away. The old woman's daughter sat there and her teeth began chattering. Then Morozko came leaping through the forest from tree to tree, snapping and cracking as he went. He looked down at the old woman's daughter:

"Are you warm, my girl?"

"Icy cold. Don't snap, Morozko! Don't crack!"

Morozko started to come down the tree and the snapping and cracking grew stronger:

"Are you warm, my girl?
Are you warm, my beauty?"

"I can't feel my hands and feet. Go away, Morozko!"

Morozko came lower still, snapping and cracking all the more:

"Are you warm, my girl?
Are you warm, my beauty?
Are you warm, my sweet?"

"Simply frozen! Be off with you, Morozko, you fiend!"

At that Morozko lost his temper, and seized the girl, turning her to ice.

As soon as it was light, the old woman sent her husband off:

"Harness the sledge quickly, you old fool, and fetch my daughter back decked in gold and silver."

The old man left and from under the table the dog barked out:

"Woof, woof!
The old man's daughter will soon be wed;
the old woman's daughter is dead, dead, dead."

The woman tossed him a pie:

"Those are the wrong words.
You should say 'The old woman's daughter will come in silver and gold...'"

But the dog would not change his tune:

"Woof, woof!
The old man's daughter will soon be wed..."

Suddenly the gates creaked, the old woman rushed out to greet her child. She turned back the blanket, and there was her daughter dead in the sledge.

The old woman howled and wailed, but it was too late.

Ivan-Tsarevich and the Grey Wolf

Once upon a time there was a tsar named Berendéi who had three sons, the youngest of which was named Ivan. Now this Tsar had a splendid garden and the most splendid thing about it was an apple-tree with golden apples.

Somebody began to visit the Tsar's garden and steal the golden apples. The Tsar was upset and sent guards to keep watch over the garden. Yet however many he sent, they could not catch the thief. The Tsar became quite tormented by this business and even stopped eating and drinking. His sons tried to comfort him:

"Dear father, do not despair, we shall go and keep watch ourselves."

The eldest son said:

"Tonight it is my turn. I shall go and guard the garden from the thief."

And off he went. For all his prowling about that evening, he did not see anyone. Eventually he lay down on the soft grass and fell asleep.

In the morning the Tsar asked him:

"Well, do you have any good news for me? Did you see the thief?"

"No, father dear, I stayed awake the whole night, never closed an eye, but I saw no-one."

The next night the middle son went to keep watch. He too slept the whole night through and in the morning said he had not seen the thief. The time came for the youngest son to go and keep watch. Ivan went to guard his father's garden and was afraid even to sit, let alone lie down. When he felt his eyelids becoming heavy, he washed them with dew from the grass and was wide awake again. He had watched half the night when suddenly it seemed to him that there was a light in the garden. It grew brighter and brighter until the whole place was lit up. There on the apple-tree he saw the Fire-Bird pecking at the golden fruit. Ivan-Tsarevich crept quietly up to the tree and grabbed the bird by its tail. The Fire-Bird took fright and flew away, leaving Ivan with a single tail feather in his hand. In the morning Ivan-Tsarevich came to his father.

"Well, my dear son, did you see the thief?"

"Father dear, I did not catch him, but, yes, I saw who is ruining our garden. Here I have brought you a memento of the thief. It is the Fire-Bird!"

The Tsar took the feather and from that moment he started eating and drinking again and forgot about his sorrow. After a while he began thinking about the Fire-Bird. He called his sons to him and said:

"My dear children, why don't you saddle up some good horses and ride out into the world, have a look what it is like and see if you can find this Fire-Bird."

The three brothers took their leave, saddled up three good horses and set out, the eldest in one direction, the next in another, and Ivan-Tsarevich in a third. Ivan-Tsarevich rode for quite a time. It was a warm summer's day and he began to feel tired. He climbed down from his horse, tied it up and dropped off to sleep. After a while, Ivan woke and realised that his horse had gone. He set off to look for it, walked and walked, and finally found a heap of bare bones — all that remained of his steed. Ivan-Tsarevich was dismayed. He had so far to go and now he was without a horse.

"Well, so what," he though to himself. "I said I would, so I shall have to." And he set off on foot. He walked and walked until he was exhausted. Then he slumped down on the soft grass and hung his head.

From out of nowhere a grey wolf came running up to him:

"Why do you sit and hang your head, Ivan-Tsarevich?"

"I've every reason to be sad, Grey Wolf. I have lost my good horse."

"It was I, Ivan-Tsarevich, who ate your horse... I am sorry for you. Tell me, why were you travelling so far and whither are you bound?"

"My father sent me out to travel the world and to find the Fire-Bird."

"Huh! You and your good horse would never have reached the Fire-Bird in three years. I alone know where it lives. Very well — I have eaten your horse, so I shall serve you loyally and truly. Get on my back and hold tight."

Ivan-Tsarevich climbed onto the beast's back and the Grey Wolf took off at such a pace that the forests were a mere blur and the lakes swept past beneath his tail. After a long time, or maybe a short one, they reached a tall fortress. The Grey Wolf stopped and said:

"Listen carefully, Ivan-Tsarevich, and heed my words. You must climb over the wall — don't worry; this is a good moment as all the guards are asleep. In a tower you will see a window; in the window stands a golden cage and in the cage the Fire-Bird sits. Take the bird, tuck it into the breast of your clothing, but be sure not to touch the cage!"

Ivan-Tsarevich climbed the wall and saw the tower. A golden cage did indeed stand in the window and there inside was the Fire-Bird. He took the bird, tucked it into the breast of his clothing and then looked at the cage. He looked and marvelled. "How beautiful and how costly it is! What a shame not to take it," he thought — and forgot what the wolf had said. The moment his hand touched the cage, the fortress was filled with noise: trumpets sounded, drums rolled, the guards awoke. They seized Ivan-Tsarevich and brought him before Tsar Afron. Tsar Afron was enraged and demanded to know who he was and where he came from.

"I am Tsar Berendei's son, Ivan-Tsarevich."

"What a disgrace! A Tsar's son who goes out thieving!"

"And what about your bird that came and plundered our garden?"

"If you had come to me and asked properly, I would have given the bird to you out of respect for your parent, Tsar Berendei — but now I shall have it cried everywhere that you are a rogue... Very well, if you perform one task for me, I shall forgive you. In such-and-such a kingdom Tsar Kusman has a horse with a golden mane. Bring me that horse and I shall give you the Fire-Bird and the cage as well."

Ivan-Tsarevich went back downcast to find the Grey Wolf. And the wolf said:

"I told you not to touch the cage! Why didn't you heed my instructions?"

"I'm sorry. Forgive me, Grey Wolf."

"Sorry, is it... Oh well, get on my back again. Never let it be said that I leave things half done."

Again the Grey Wolf ran off with Ivan-Tsarevich. After a long time, or maybe a short one, they reached the fortress where the horse with the golden mane was to be found.

"Climb over the wall, Ivan-Tsarevich, while the guards are sleeping. Go to the stables, take the horse, but on no account touch the bridle!"

Ivan climbed into the fortress. All the guards were asleep. He made his way into the stables, found the horse with the golden mane, but then he caught sight of the bridle — it was made of gold and decorated with precious stones, indeed nothing else would have done for such a stallion. Ivan-Tsarevich reached for the bridle and the fortress was filled with noise: trumpets sounded, drums rolled, the guards awoke. They seized Ivan-Tsarevich and brought him before Tsar Kusman.

"Who are you and where are you from?"

"I am Ivan-Tsarevich."

"Well, well, and look what you are up to! Horse-stealing — even a common peasant would know better than that. Very well, if you perform one task for me, I shall forgive you. Tsar Dalmat has a daughter they call Yelena the Beautiful. Carry her off and bring her to me and I shall give you the horse with the golden mane and the bridle as well."

Ivan-Tsarevich went back even more downcast to find the Grey Wolf.

"I told you not to touch the bridle. Why didn't you heed my instructions?"

"I'm sorry. Forgive me, Grey Wolf."

"Sorry, is it... Oh well, get on my back again."

Again the Grey Wolf sped off with Ivan-Tsarevich. They ran as far as Tsar Dalmat's fortress and there in the garden Yelena the Beautiful was accustomed to walk with her nurses and nannies. The Grey Wolf said:

"This time I shall leave you here and go myself. Start back the way we came and I shall soon catch up with you."

Ivan-Tsarevich set off back the way they had come, while the Grey Wolf leapt over the wall and into the garden. He crouched behind a bush and waited... Yelena the Beautiful came out with her nannies and nurses. They strolled and strolled, but the moment Yelena the Beautiful fell a little behind her nurses and nannies, the Grey Wolf pounced, tossed her over his back and was gone. Ivan-Tsarevich was walking along, when suddenly the Grey Wolf caught up with him and there on the wolf's back was Yelena the Beautiful. Ivan-Tsarevich was overjoyed, but the Grey Wolf said:

"Get on my back quickly, in case they come after us!"

The Grey Wolf tore along with Ivan-Tsarevich and Yelena the Beautiful on his back. He moved at such a pace that the forests were a mere blur and the lakes and

rivers swept past beneath his tail. After a long time, or maybe a short one, they approached Tsar Kusman's fortress.

The Grey Wolf asked:

"Why so quiet, Ivan-Tsarevich? Is there something troubling you?"

"Of course I am unhappy, Grey Wolf. How can I bear to part with such a maiden? How can I exchange Yelena the Beautiful for a horse?"

The Grey Wolf replied:

"I won't part you from such beauty. We shall hide her somewhere here. I shall turn myself into Yelena the Beautiful and you bring me to the Tsar."

So they hid Yelena the Beautiful in a hut in the forest. The Grey Wolf turned head-over-heels and became the spit and image of Yelena the Beautiful. Ivan-Tsarevich brought her to Tsar Kusman. The Tsar was delighted and thanked him profusely:

"Thank you, Ivan-Tsarevich, for bringing me my bride. Take the horse with the golden mane and the bridle as well."

Ivan-Tsarevich mounted the magnificent animal and rode back to Yelena the Beautiful. He sat her before him on the horse and rode on. Tsar Kusman meanwhile arranged his wedding. The feasting went on into the evening and when it came time he carried his bride up to the bedchamber. He laid her down on the bed and as he looked into her face he saw — a wolf's snout and fangs! The Tsar staggered back in fear and the wolf made good his escape.

The Grey Wolf caught up with Ivan-Tsarevich and asked him:

"Is something troubling you?"

"Of course, Grey Wolf. How can I bear to part with such a treasure? How can I exchange the horse with a golden mane for the Fire-Bird?"

"Don't despair, I shall help you."

So, as they approached Tsar Afron's fortress, the wolf said:

"You hide this horse and Yelena the Beautiful. I shall turn myself into the horse with the golden mane and you bring me to the Tsar."

They hid Yelena the Beautiful and the horse with the golden mane in the forest. The Grey Wolf turned head-over-heels and became the spit and image of the horse with the golden mane. Ivan-Tsarevich brought it to Tsar Afron. The Tsar was delighted and gave him the Fire-Bird together with its golden cage. Ivan-Tsarevich returned on foot to the forest, sat Yelena the Beautiful on the horse with the golden mane, took up the Fire-Bird in its golden cage and rode off towards his own country. Meanwhile Tsar Afron gave orders for the horse to be brought out and was about to mount, when it turned back into the Grey Wolf. The Tsar staggered back in fear and the Grey Wolf made good his escape. Soon he caught up with Ivan-Tsarevich and said:

"Now I bid you farewell, as I can go no further."

Ivan-Tsarevich sprang from his horse and bowed deeply three times, thanking the Grey Wolf with great respect. But the wolf said:

"Do not take your last leave of me, you will have need of me again."

Ivan-Tsarevich thought, "What more need can I have of him? All my wishes have come true."

He mounted the horse with the golden mane and rode on with Yelena the Beautiful and the Fire-Bird. When he reached familiar places, he decided to stop for lunch. He had a little food with him and they washed it down with cool spring water. Then they lay down to rest. As soon as Ivan-Tsarevich had fallen asleep, his brothers came riding up. They had travelled through other lands, seeking the Fire-Bird and were now returning empty-handed. When they saw everything that Ivan-Tsarevich was bringing back, they began to plot:

"Let us kill our brother and all this will be ours."

And they did kill Ivan-Tsarevich, mounted the horse with the golden mane and took the Fire-Bird. They put Yelena the Beautiful on one of their own horses and threatened her with terrible things if she spoke a word of what they had done.

Ivan-Tsarevich lay dead and the crows were already gathering, when from out of nowhere the Grey Wolf appeared, seizing a great crow and one of its young.

"You, crow, fly and fetch living and dead water. If you bring me water, both living and dead, I shall let your youngster go."

The crow had no choice but to do so, as the wolf kept tight hold of the fledgling. After a time the bird came back with living and dead water. The Grey Wolf sprinkled dead water on Ivan-Tsarevich's wounds and they healed. He then sprinkled the prince with living water and Ivan-Tsarevich came back to life.

"Oh, how deeply I slept!"

"Deep indeed," said the wolf. "Had it not been for me, you would never have woken. Your own brothers killed you and carried off all you had gained. Get on my back quickly!"

They went chasing after Ivan's brothers and when they caught up with them the Grey Wolf tore them both apart and scattered the pieces in all directions. Ivan-Tsarevich bowed again to the Grey Wolf and took his leave of him for ever.

The prince returned home on the horse with the golden mane, bringing the Fire-Bird for his father and Yelena the Beautiful for himself. Tsar Berendei was delighted and began to ask his son about his adventures. Ivan-Tsarevich told him how the Grey Wolf had helped him, how his brothers had killed him as he slept, and how the Grey Wolf had torn them to pieces.

The Tsar was saddened, but soon comforted. Ivan-Tsarevich married Yelena the Beautiful and they lived happily ever after.

The King of the Sea
and Vasilisa the Wise

Once upon a time, in a country far away, there lived a Tsar and his Tsarina who had no children. The Tsar went off on a long journey to distant lands and while he was away the Tsarina gave birth to a son, whom she called Ivan-Tsarevich, or Prince Ivan. The Tsar, however, did not know that he had become a father.

He began his return journey and, as he approached his own country, the sun began to beat down, and the air was hot and dry. The tsar was tormented by thirst and would have given anything just for a drink. He looked around and not far away he spotted a large lake. He rode down to the lake, jumped from his horse, lay down flat on the bank and began to lap up the icy cold water. He drank and drank, never suspecting the trouble he was in — for the King of the Sea had seized him by the beard.

"Let me go," the Tsar begged.

"No I will not. How dare you drink my water without permission?"

"I'll give you anything you ask, only let me go."

"Give me the thing that you do not know at home."

The Tsar thought and thought — what was there at home that he did not know? He was sure that he knew everything, that everything was familiar — and so he agreed. He lifted his head and his beard came free of the water. He got up, mounted his horse and returned home.

As he rode up, the Tsarina came out to meet him, holding their son. She was full of joy, but, when he heard of his son's birth, the Tsar shed bitter tears. He told his wife what had happened to him and they wept together. But there was nothing to be done — it's no use, as they say, crying over spilt milk.

They went back to their life together. The prince seemed to grow as they watched and before any time at all had passed he was a fine young man.

"However long we keep him, we shall have to give him up in the end," the Tsar thought and decided to have done with it. He took Ivan-Tsarevich by the hand and led him straight to the fateful lake.

"Search here for my ring," he told him. "I dropped it here yesterday."

He left the prince alone and went back home.

Ivan began looking for the ring. As he walked along the lakeshore, an old woman came from the opposite direction.

"Where are you going, Ivan-Tsarevich."

"Don't bother me, old witch. Be off with you, things are bad enough already."

"In that case, good day to you." The old woman walked away.

Then Ivan-Tsarevich thought better of what he had done.

"Why was I rude to the old woman? I'll call her back. Old people can be quick-witted and cunning. She might tell me something useful." And he shouted after her:

"Come back, good woman, forgive my hasty words! I spoke out of vexation. My father left me here to search for his ring and I cannot find it for all my looking!"

"It's not on account of a ring that you are here, Ivan-Tsarevich. Your father has

given you up to the King of the Sea. The King will come out and take you back with him to his underwater kingdom."

The prince burst into tears.

"Don't despair, Ivan-Tsarevich! Your luck may still change, if you listen well to what an old woman tells you. Hide behind that currant-bush and stay quiet. A dozen doves will land here, all beautiful maidens, and they will be followed by a thirteenth. All will go to bathe in the lake. While they are bathing, you take the thirteenth's shift and be sure to keep it until she gives you her ring. If you fail, you will be lost for ever. A high wall of stakes, fully ten versts long, surrounds the King of the Sea's palace, and on the top of each stake is a head. One alone remains unoccupied. Don't let your head end up on it!"

Ivan-Tsarevich thanked the old woman, got down behind the currant bush and waited for what would happen.

Suddenly twelve doves came out of the air and, as they touched the earth, they turned into beautiful maidens, each fairer in face and body than can be imagined or described. They shook off their dresses and entered the lake, where they splashed and played, laughed and sang.

Soon a thirteenth dove flew down and turned into a beautiful maiden as it touched the ground. She threw the shift off her milk-white body and went to bathe. This maiden was fairer and lovelier than all the rest!

For a long time Ivan-Tsarevich was unable to tear his eyes away from her. He stared and stared, but then he remembered what the old woman had told him. He crept up and took her shift.

The beautiful maiden came out of the water and could not find her shift. Someone must have taken it. All the maidens looked, but it was nowhere to be found.

"Search no more, dear sisters! Fly away home. It is my fault. I did not keep my eye on it and I must take the blame."

The beautiful maiden sisters struck the ground, turned back into doves, spread their wings and flew away. Left alone, the maiden looked all around and said aloud:

"Come out with my shift, whoever you are. If you are an old man you will be like a father to me. If you are of middle age, you will be a favourite brother. And if you are of my own age, you will be my dear sweetheart."

As soon as the words were out, Ivan-Tsarevich showed himself. She gave him her gold ring and said:

"Oh, Ivan-Tsarevich, why have you been so long in coming? The King of the Sea is furious with you. There is the road that leads to the underwater kingdom: follow it and don't be afraid. You will find me there too, for I am Vasilísa the Wise, daughter of the King of the Sea."

Vasilisa turned herself into a bird and flew off, leaving the prince alone.

Ivan-Tsarevich made his way into the underwater kingdom. He saw that the light is the same there as with us. There are fields and meadows and green groves and the sun shines warm.

He presented himself to the King of the Sea and the King thundered at him:

"Why have you been so long in coming? To make up for it, here is what you have to do: I have a piece of waste land thirty versts long and thirty wide, full of pits, gullies and sharp stones. Tomorrow I want to see it as flat as my hand and sown with rye that by early morning has grown so high that a jackdaw can hide in it. And if you fail, your head will fly from your shoulders!"

Ivan-Tsarevich left the King of the Sea and burst into tears. Vasilisa the Wise saw him from her room high in the palace and called to him:

"Greetings, Ivan-Tsarevich! Why so miserable?"

"How can I be anything else but miserable?" the prince replied. "The King of the Sea has ordered me to fill in the pits and gullies, remove the stones, and sow the field with rye that by morning should be so high that a jackdaw can hide in it."

"That is no trouble; the trouble is yet to come. Lie down and sleep peacefully. In the morning everything will be as it should be."

Ivan-Tsarevich went to bed, and Vasilisa the Wise came out onto the porch and shouted in a loud voice:

"Hey, my loyal servants! Level the deep pits, remove the sharp stones and sow the field with rye so that it ripens by morning."

Ivan-Tsarevich awoke with the dawn. He looked out and everything was done: no pits or gullies, the field was as smooth as your hand and full of rye tall enough to hide a jackdaw.

He went and reported to the King of the Sea.

"I thank you for that service," the King said. "Here is another task: I have three hundred shocks, each containing three hundred sheaves — all of fine corn. Take out all the corn, down to the very last grain, for me by tomorrow, but do not break up the shocks or take the sheaves apart. If you fail, your head will fly from your shoulders!"

"Yes, Your Majesty," Ivan-Tsarevich replied.

Again he turned and went away in tears.

"Why so miserable?" Vasilisa the Wise asked him.

"How can I be anything else but miserable? The King of the Sea has ordered me to collect all the corn in a single night, without losing a single grain, breaking up the shocks or taking the sheaves apart."

"That is no trouble; the trouble is yet to come. Lie down and sleep peacefully. In the morning everything will be as it should be."

Ivan-Tsarevich went to bed, and Vasilisa the Wise came out onto the porch and shouted in a loud voice:

"Hey, you creeping ants! However many of you there are in the world, all come here and bring the corn from my father's shocks, down to the very last grain."

In the morning the King of the Sea summoned Ivan-Tsarevich.

"Well, have you performed that task?"

"I have, Your Majesty."

"Let's go and see."

They went to the threshing barn. All the shocks were still standing whole and unbroken. They went to the granaries. All the bins were full to the brim with grain.

"Thank you, son," said the King of the Sea. "If you can make me a church of pure wax by tomorrow morning, that will be your last task."

Again Ivan-Tsarevich went away with tears in his eyes.

"Why so miserable?" Vasilisa the Wise asked him from her high window.

"How can I be anything else but miserable? The King of the Sea has ordered me to build a church of pure wax in a single night.

"That is no trouble; the trouble is yet to come. Lie down and sleep peacefully. In the morning everything will be as it should be."

Ivan-Tsarevich went to bed, and Vasilisa the Wise came out onto the porch and shouted in a loud voice:

"Hey, you busy bees! However many of you there are in the world, all come here and build a church out of pure wax by the morning."

In the morning Ivan-Tsarevich awoke, looked out and there was a church of pure wax. He went and reported to the King of the Sea.

"Thank you, Ivan-Tsarevich. Of all the servants I have ever had, none has pleased me as greatly as you. For that you shall be my heir, the guardian of the whole realm, and choose any of my thirteen daughters to be your wife."

Ivan-Tsarevich chose Vasilisa the Wise. They were married at once and the feasting and celebrations went on for three whole days.

After some time had passed, Ivan-Tsarevich began to miss his parents and to long to see the holy land of Russia once more.

"Why so miserable, Ivan-Tsarevich?"

"Oh, Vasilisa, I am missing my father and my mother; I want to go back to Holy Russia."

"There we are: the trouble has come! If we leave, there will be a great hunt for us. The King of the Sea will be furious and have us put to death. We shall have to be cunning."

Vasilisa spat in three corners of their room, locked the door and hurried off with Ivan-Tsarevich in the direction of Holy Russia.

Early the next day messengers came to summon the young couple to the King of the Sea. They knocked on the door and called out:

"Wake up. Arise. The King has summoned you!"

"It's still early. We haven't finished sleeping. Come back later," one drop of spit answered.

The messengers went away, waited for an hour or two and then knocked again:

"It's time to stop sleeping and get up!"

"Wait a little. We're getting up and dressing," the second drop of spit replied.

The messengers came back a third time to say that the King was angry because they were taking so long.

"We're just coming," the third drop of spit answered.

The messengers waited and waited. They knocked again and when they got no response, they broke down the door and found the room empty.

When they told the King that the young couple had fled, he flew into a rage and raised a great hue and cry for them.

But Vasilisa the Wise and Ivan-Tsarevich were already far away. They drove their swift-footed steeds on without pausing to rest.

"Ivan-Tsarevich, put your ear to the ground and listen whether the King of the

Sea has sent his people after us."

Ivan-Tsarevich leapt from his horse, put his ear to the ground and said:

"I can hear talking and the beat of hooves."

"They are coming after us," said Vasilisa the Wise and instantly changed the horses into a green meadow, Ivan-Tsarevich into an old shepherd and herself into a quietly grazing sheep.

The pursuers rode up to them:

"Hey, old shepherd, have you seen a fine young man and a beautiful girl ride by here?"

"No, I have not, good sirs," Ivan-Tsarevich replied. "In the forty years I have been tending my sheep here, not a single bird has flown by, nor a single beast run by."

The pursuers turned back:

"Your Majesty, we found no-one on the road and saw only an old shepherd tending a sheep."

"Why didn't you seize them — that was Ivan and Vasilisa," the King shouted and sent his men out again.

Meanwhile Ivan-Tsarevich and Vasilisa the Wise were back on their horses and riding like the wind.

"Ivan-Tsarevich, put your ear to the ground and listen whether the King of the Sea has sent his people after us."

Ivan-Tsarevich leapt from his horse, put his ear to the ground and said:

"I can hear talking and the beat of hooves."

"They are coming after us," said Vasilisa the Wise. She changed herself into a church, Ivan-Tsarevich into an old priest and the horses into trees.

The pursuers rode up to them:

"Hey, Father, have you seen a shepherd and a sheep go by here?"

"No, I haven't, good sirs. In the forty years I have been working in this church, not a single bird has flown by, nor a single beast run by."

The pursuers turned back:

"Your Majesty, we could not find the shepherd and the sheep anywhere. All that we saw on the way was a church with an old priest."

"Why didn't you smash down the church and seize the priest? That was Ivan and Vasilisa!" the King of the Sea fumed and mounted up himself to chase after Ivan-Tsarevich and Vasilisa the Wise.

Meanwhile they were even farther on.

Again Vasilisa the Wise said:

"Ivan-Tsarevich, put your ear to the ground and listen whether the King of the Sea has sent his people after us."

Ivan-Tsarevich leapt from his horse, put his ear to the ground and said:

"I can hear talking and the beat of hooves stronger than before."

"It's the King himself riding after us."

Vasilisa the Wise turned the horses into a lake, herself into a duck and Ivan-Tsarevich into a drake. The King of the Sea rode up to the lake and immediately realised who the duck and drake really were. He struck the ground and turned himself into an eagle. The eagle tried to kill them, but could not manage it...

Each time he plunged down on them, at the last instant they dived beneath the water. Again and again he attacked; again and again they slipped away. In the end the King rode back to his underwater kingdom. Vasilisa the Wise and Ivan-Tsarevich waited a good while and then rode on to Holy Russia.

Eventually they came to Ivan-Tsarevich's own land.

"Wait for me here in this little wood," he told Vasilisa the Wise.

"I will go ahead and announce our arrival to father and mother."

"You will forget me, Ivan-Tsarevich!"

"No, I won't."

"You will, Ivan-Tsarevich. Remember me at least when two doves start tapping on the window."

Ivan-Tsarevich entered the palace. His parents saw him and rushed to embrace him. In his happiness the prince forgot about Vasilisa the Wise. He lived one day with his father and mother, then a second, and on the third he began thinking of courting some princess.

Vasilisa the Wise went into the town and took work with a woman who baked the communion bread. They began to prepare the Host and she took two small pieces of dough, fashioned them into doves and put them in the oven.

"Guess what will become of those doves, mistress."

"What will become of them? We'll eat them, of course."

"No, you guessed wrong!"

Vasilisa the Wise opened the oven, flung the window wide, and in an instant the doves spread their wings, flew straight to the palace and began to tap on the windows. Try as they might, the Tsar's servants could not drive them off.

Then Ivan-Tsarevich remembered about Vasilisa the Wise. He sent messengers out in all directions to find her and discovered her with the woman who baked the Host. He took her by the hands, kissed her on the lips and brought her to his mother and father. The young couple moved into the palace and they all lived happily ever after.

The Swan-Geese

A peasant man lived with his wife in a village. They had a daughter and a son who was still quite small.

One day the mother said: "Daughter, we are going to work now. Look after your little brother. Don't leave the yard and if you are a good girl we will buy you a shawl."

The mother and father went off and soon the girl forgot what she had been told. She sat her little brother down on the grass in the yard, and went out into the street where she got so involved in a game that she wandered farther and farther from home.

Meanwhile the swan-geese came flying by, seized the boy and carried him off with them.

At last the girl came back, only to find her brother gone. She groaned and rushed about, looking everywhere. She called him, cried and threatened him with what would happen when their parents returned, but the boy did not appear.

She ran out into the open country and then, way off in the distance, she spotted the swan-geese just as they disappeared behind the dark forest. She guessed that they must have taken her brother away. It had long been said that the swan-geese were fond of such tricks as carrying off little children.

The girl went chasing after them.

She ran and ran until she came to a stove.

"Stove, o stove, tell me where the swan-geese have flown."

The stove replied:

"Eat some of my rye cake and I shall tell you."

"I'll not eat rye cakes. In my father's house we do not even eat wheat cakes."

The stove did not tell her.

The girl ran on until she came to an apple-tree.

"Apple-tree, o apple-tree, tell me where the swan-geese have flown."

"Eat my crab apples and I shall tell you."

"In my father's house we do not even eat apples from the orchard."

The apple-tree did not tell her.

The girl ran on until she came to a river of milk flowing through banks of kissél, which is a kind of starchy jelly.

"O river of milk, o banks of kissel, tell me where the swan-geese have flown."

"Eat my plain kissel with milk and I shall tell you."

"In my father's house we do not even eat cream."

She ran on for a long, long way, through fields and woods. The daylight was beginning to fade and soon she would have no choice but to turn for home. Then suddenly she saw a hut standing on chicken legs. It had a single window and was turning round in circles.

Inside the old witch Baba-Yaga sat spinning flax. And on the bench there sat her brother playing with silver apples. The girl went into the hut.

"Good evening."

"Good evening, girl. Why have you come?"

"I have been walking in the moss, over the marshes. My dress is wet and I came to get warm."

"Sit down then and spin for a while."

Baba-Yaga gave her the spindle and went outside. The girl started spinning and suddenly a little mouse popped out from under the stove and said:

"Girl, give me some porridge and I will tell you something you should know."

The girl gave the mouse some porridge and it said:

"Baba-Yaga has gone to stoke the fire in the bathhouse. She'll wash you clean then put you in the oven, roast you and eat you. Later she will roll around on your bones."

The girl sat frozen to the spot with tears running down her cheeks.

The mouse went on:

"Don't wait. Take your brother and run. I shall spin the flax for you."

The girl grabbed her brother and ran. Baba-Yaga came up to the window of the hut and called inside:

"Girl, are you spinning?"

"Yes, I am," the mouse replied.

Baba-Yaga finished heating the bathhouse and went to fetch the girl. But there was no-one in the hut.

Baba-Yaga shouted out:

"Swan-Geese, after them! The girl has carried her brother off!"

Brother and sister ran to the river of milk. Then the girl spotted the swan-geese flying after them.

"River, dear river, hide me!"

"Eat my plain kissel."

The girl ate it and said thank you. The river hid her under its banks of kissel. The swan-geese could not see the girl and flew on by.

The girl and her brother continued running, but the swan-geese turned round and came flying back towards them. Any moment they would spot them. There was nothing left to hope for, and then they came to the apple-tree.

"Apple-tree, dear apple-tree, hide me!"

"Eat my crab apples."

The girl ate as quickly as she could and said thank you. The apple-tree wrapped her in its branches and covered her with its leaves. The swan-geese could not see the girl and flew on by.

The girl sped on again. She ran and ran, and, when there was only a little way to go, the swan-geese spotted her. They cackled loudly, beat the air with their wings and were on the point of snatching the boy from his sister's arms when she reached the stove.

"Stove, dear stove, hide me!"

"Eat some of my rye cake."

The girl popped the cake into her mouth as quick as she could, then climbed into the stove with her brother, and sat where the fire would be. The swan-geese dived and circled, honked and screeched, but in the end they had to admit defeat and fly back to Baba-Yaga.

The girl thanked the stove and ran home with her brother. Just as they reached the house, their mother and father came back.

Nikita the Tanner

Russian people lived in the city of Kiev. They built houses, laid out their gardens, tilled the soil and sang songs. All of a sudden, from lands unknown, Gorynych the dragon came to Kiev. His body was green, his eyes red, his wings were made of iron, his claws of bronze. Ten heads and ten trunks were attached to snake-like necks. The dragon roared and hissed so dreadfully that the leaves flew from the trees.

"I shall burn this city of Kiev, I shall slay all the people, I shall dig up all the earth. If you want to remain alive, then every month give me a beautiful maiden — a meal for me, salvation for you!"

What could they do? How can you fight against such a monster?

The people groaned and wept, but there was nothing for it but to give Gorynych the dragon a maiden each month. They took the beautiful girl to the top of a tall hill and attached her to an oak with chains. Gorynych tore the century-old oak out by the roots, carried it away to his lair, snapped the chains and devoured the maiden.

Before very long he had devoured all the maidens in the city. Only the Tsar's daughter remained. The time came when she had to go and be eaten by the dragon. The Tsar wept, the Tsarina howled. The city was hung with black flags and the whole country groaned.

They took the princess to the tall hill and fastened her to an oak with chains of gold. There she stood, more dead than alive. Her light brown plait had come loose and hung down to her knees. Then Gorynych came flying down. He saw her incomparable beauty and forgot about eating her. He tore the chains from her, sat her on one iron wing and carried her off to his lair.

"You will stay here," he told her, "and keep house for me."

She found that idea even worse than death. One day passed, and a second day dawned. The dragon wanted to go about his business and so he sealed the princess up inside the cave with century-old oaks to prevent her getting away. He wove the branches and twisted the trunks together so that no man could pass through, nor even a beast.

In her room at the palace the princess had kept a grey-winged, blue-breasted dove. Now he went flying over the woods and fields, constantly seeking his lost mistress. He passed the dragon's lair just as the princess was singing a sad song. On hearing her voice, the dove flew to the cave, found a tiny gap between the green branches and squeezed through into the dragon's lair. He crumpled his wing a little, but he reached the princess.

How pleased she was to see him! She talked and talked. She asked about everything — how were her mother and father, what was happening in Kiev, were the flowers blooming in the meadows, was the corn growing in the fields,

were the larks singing in the sky? You see, in that dark cave she could not see or hear anything — the breeze did not reach her; the sun did not warm her.

The dove told here everything she wanted to know and as evening approached he flew away. He began to come every day, bringing the princess news from the Tsar and Tsarina, and telling her everything that was going on in the world. Then one day the dove said:

"Your father, the Tsar, asks you to try to find out from the dragon whether there is anything in the world more powerful than him."

In the evening the dragon flew back and tossed aside the century-old oaks at the mouth of the cave. Their thick branches snapped like threads, their trunks bent like straws. And the princess said to him:

"Oh, how strong you are, Gorynych! There is probably nothing in the world stronger than you!"

The dragon replied:

"In Kiev there is a man stronger than me — Nikita the Tanner who lives in the Leather-Workers' quarter. If Nikita starts to stoke the stove the smoke rises up to the clouds; if Nikita goes down to the Dnieper to soak ox-hides he carries not one, but a dozen at once. When the hides had swollen with water, I swam up and fastened on to them. Well, I thought, now he won't be able to pull the hides out of the river — they have become awfully heavy. And he didn't care... rolls up his sleeves, plants his feet apart and very nearly pulls me up onto the bank. There you are — Nikita the Tanner is the one thing in the world that I fear."

The princess made no response to what the dragon said, as if she had not been listening. The next day, when the dove came, she said to him:

"My grey-winged, blue-breasted dove, tell my father, the Tsar, that Nikita the Tanner who lives in the Leather-Workers' quarter in Kiev is stronger than Gorynych the dragon."

When the Tsar heard about Nikita the Tanner, he went himself to the Leather Workers' quarter. Nikita was busy kneading hides. When he caught sight of the Tsar, he began to tremble with fright. His hands shook and he tore a dozen ox-hides into little pieces, leaving nothing but thin strips. The Tsar saw that and was astonished. He had never heard of such strength.

"Well, Nikita the Tanner," the Tsar said, "you certainly are strong. You alone can deal with the dragon. Deliver the world from Gorynych, and save my daughter, the Princess Maryúshka."

Nikita the Tanner just stood and shook, his knees growing weak with fear.

"But, Your Majesty," he said, "I am a timid man, how am I to deal with the dragon?"

The Tsar tried everything he could think of to persuade him — silver, gold, the finest pearls — but Nikita remained as reluctant as ever. The Tsar then gathered together five thousand small children. They went down on their knees in front of Nikita, crying, wailing, and pouring out tears:

"Have pity on us, dear Nikita: a few years will pass and we too will all go to be eaten by the accursed dragon. Have pity on us, rescue us, Nikita!"

Nikita had pity on them and gave his consent. And so he began to prepare for the battle. Nikita took three hundred poods of hemp, soaked it in pitch and wrapped himself in it from head to foot. Then he covered himself with ox-hides and went out to meet Gorynych. The dragon heard that Nikita was coming and sealed himself up in his lair. He set about sharpening his teeth and pointing his claws.

Nikita shouted in a loud voice:

"Come out in the open, monster, and fight honestly, otherwise I shall destroy your lair and kill you where you hide!"

With that he began slashing at the century-old oaks with such force that they broke into splinters. The dragon sprang out of its cave and they began to fight. The very earth trembled and the trees shook from their roots. The dragon lunged and grabbed Nikita in his teeth. He tore off a piece of ox-hide and his teeth caught in the pitch-soaked hemp, but Nikita was unhurt. Nikita hit the dragon with a great club that weighed fully ten poods. With every blow the creature sank further into the ground. He struck again and again until Gorynych rolled over and he planted his foot on him. Then the dragon began to whimper and begged:

"Do not beat me to death, Nikita the Tanner. There is no-one stronger than us in the whole world. Let us divide up the whole Earth equally between us — you rule in one half and I shall live out my days in the other."

"Very well," the tanner said, "but there must be a boundary line drawn between us."

Nikita forged a plough weighing three hundred poods, harnessed the dragon to it and started to plough a furrow from Kiev. The dragon pulled the plough, panting and puffing, while Nikita rode on top, driving the dragon on with a switch:

"Hey, Gorynych, keep the furrow straight!"

So Nikita the Tanner drew his boundary line from Kiev to the Caspian Sea.

"Well," the dragon said, "now you and I have divided up the whole Earth."

"We've divided the earth," Nikita said. "Now let's divide the sea. Otherwise you'll be saying that I am taking your water, or soaking my skins in it."

Nikita drove the dragon out into the Caspian Sea. The three-hundred-pood plough was dragging Gorynych to the bottom and Nikita the Tanner helped him on his way with blows from his iron club, saying:

"Keep the furrow straight, dragon. Plough the water deeper."

Gorynych the dragon struggled and struggled, and finally drowned in the middle of the sea. Afterwards Nikita dragged his body to the shore, so that the monster would not spoil the water.

He built a fire and burnt the dragon, scattering the ashes to the winds. That was a mistake — he should have buried the ashes, for as soon as the wind caught them they turned into flies, mosquitoes, midges and other creatures that trouble people in summer to this day. And off they went humming and buzzing around the world.

If Nikita had only buried the ashes in the ground, we would have been spared all that discomfort.

Anyway, that is how Nikita the Tanner delivered the Russian land from the dragon. He broke down the monster's lair, released the princess and took her back to her mother and father. The Tsar and Tsarina wept for joy. Throughout Kiev people rejoiced, sang and praised Nikita. They brought the tanner silver, gold, the finest pearls, expensive clothes and good things to eat.

Nikita wanted none of it. He only took a crust of bread and an onion and went back to the Leather Workers' quarter to knead his ox-hides.

The Peasant and the Bear

A peasant went into the forest to plant turnips. He cleared a plot and dug it over. Just as he was finishing, a bear came up to him and said:

"Man, I am going to thrash you."

"Don't thrash me, dear bear. You'd do better to let me plant my turnips. When they grow, we'll share. You take the tops, but let me at least keep the roots."

"Very well," said the bear. "But if you deceive me, you had better not show your face in the forest again."

With that he turned and went back into the thick forest.

The turnips grew large and in the autumn the peasant came with his cart to dig them up. The bear limbered out of the thick forest:

"Well, man, the time has come to divide the turnips. Give me my share."

"Very well, dear bear, let's share: the tops for you, the roots for me."

The peasant gave the bear all the leafy tops, put the turnips on his cart and took them off to town to sell. On the way he came across the bear again:

"Where are you going, man?"

"I am going to town, dear bear, to sell the roots."

"Well, let my try one to see what it is like."

The peasant gave him a turnip. The bear took a big bite and roared:

"Rrrrr! You have tricked me! Your roots are nice and sweet! Don't dare come into the forest for firewood or I shall thrash you!"

The next year the peasant planted rye on the same spot.

When he came to reap it, he found the bear already waiting for him:

"You won't trick me this time, man. Give me my share."

The peasant said:

"Very well. You take the roots, dear bear, but let me at least keep the tops."

They gathered the rye. The peasant left the bear the roots, loaded the rye onto his cart and took it home. The bear tried everything, but he could not find any use for the roots. He was furious with the peasant and since then there has always been hostility between bear and man.

The Frog Princess

Long, long ago there lived a Tsar who had three sons. When all three had come of age, the Tsar called them to him and said:

"My dear children, before I grow old, I should like to see you married and to enjoy your children, my grandchildren."

The sons replied:

"Well then, father, give us your blessing. Tell us who our brides are to be."

"Do as I say, my sons. Each of you take an arrow, go out into the open countryside and shoot it. Wherever the arrow lands, there your destiny lies."

The sons left their father; each took an arrow and went out into the open countryside. They drew their bows and shot.

The eldest son's arrow fell into a boyar's courtyard and was picked up by that nobleman's daughter. The second son's arrow fell in the courtyard of a great merchant's house and was picked up by the merchant's daughter.

The youngest son, Ivan-Tsarevich, shot his arrow. It rose into the air and flew so far that he could not see where it landed. He walked and walked and at last he came to a marsh. Sitting there was a frog holding his arrow. Ivan-Tsarevich called:

"Frog, hey frog, give me back my arrow!"

But the frog replied:

"Take me as your wife!"

"What are you saying? How can I take a frog as my wife?"

"Take me — for that is your destiny."

Ivan-Tsarevich was greatly upset, but there was nothing for it. He picked up the frog and took her home. The Tsar arranged a triple wedding: his eldest son married the boyar's daughter; his second son married the merchant's daughter; and the unfortunate Ivan married the frog. Soon the Tsar called his sons to him:

"I want to see which of your wives is the best needlewoman. Have each of them sew me a shirt by tomorrow."

The sons bowed and went to their wives.

Ivan-Tsarevich came home, sat down and hung his head. The frog jumped up and asked him:

"Why are you hanging your head, Ivan-Tsarevich? Has something bad happened?"

"My father has commanded that you sew him a shirt by tomorrow."

The frog replied:

"Don't worry, Ivan-Tsarevich. You go off to bed. In the morning everything will be as it should be."

Ivan-Tsarevich went to bed, while the frog hopped out onto the porch, shed her frog's skin and turned into Vasilísa the Wise, a maiden more beautiful than can be described even in a fairy-tale. Vasilisa the Wise clapped her hands and shouted out:

"Nurses and nannies, hear me and come, for there's work to be done! Make me by morning a shirt like my own father has."

When Ivan-Tsarevich woke in the morning, the frog was already hopping around the floor. The shirt lay on the table wrapped in a towel. Ivan-Tsarevich was delighted

and took the shirt to his father. His elder brothers were just showing their wives' efforts to the Tsar. The eldest son unwrapped his shirt:

"That's a shirt fit for a lowly peasant hut."

The second son unwrapped his shirt. The Tsar said:

"That's only good for wearing to the bathhouse."

Ivan-Tsarevich unwrapped his shirt. It was embroidered with gold and silver in elaborate patterns. As soon as the Tsar saw it, he exclaimed:

"Now that is a shirt fit for a feast-day."

As Ivan's two brothers went back to their homes, they said to each other:

"You know, we were wrong to laugh at Ivan's wife. She is obviously not a frog, but some cunning creature..."

Soon the Tsar called his sons to him again:

"Have each of your wives bake me a loaf by tomorrow. I want to see which of them is the best cook."

Ivan-Tsarevich returned home with a heavy head. The frog asked him:

"Why so sad?"

He answered:

"You must bake a loaf of bread for the Tsar by tomorrow."

"Don't worry, Ivan-Tsarevich. You go off to bed. In the morning everything will be as it should be."

The other two wives, who had laughed at the frog at first, sent an old serving-woman to watch how Ivan's bride would bake bread. The frog could not be so easily caught, though. She made dough, then broke a hole right in the top of the stove and tipped all the dough straight in. The serving-woman ran to the other brides and told them what she had seen. They began to do exactly the same. Meanwhile the frog hopped out onto the porch, turned into Vasilisa the Wise and clapped her hands:

"Nurses and nannies, hear me and come, for there's work to be done! Bake me by morning a loaf of soft white bread like I used to eat in my father's house."

When Ivan-Tsarevich woke in the morning, the loaf lay on the table. It was highly decorated with patterns pressed into the sides and a model city with gates on the top. Ivan-Tsarevich was delighted, wrapped the loaf in a cloth and took it to his father. His elder brothers were just showing their wives' efforts to the Tsar. They had tipped the dough straight into the stove as the old serving-woman had told them, and of course it came out a burnt mess. The Tsar took the loaf from his eldest son, looked at it and sent it to the servants' hall. He took the loaf from his second son and promptly did the same. When Ivan-Tsarevich showed him his loaf, though, the Tsar exclaimed:

"This is a loaf that should be eaten only on a feast-day."

Without further ado, the Tsar commanded his three sons to appear the next evening with their wives at a banquet. Again Ivan-Tsarevich went home with a heavy heart, his head hanging low. The frog jumped up and asked him:

"Croak, croak. Why so sad, Ivan-Tsarevich? Has your father said something to upset you?"

"Frog, o frog, I cannot but be sad for my father has ordered me to bring you to the banquet tomorrow, and how can I show you to people?"

The frog replied:

"Don't worry, Ivan-Tsarevich. You go to the banquet alone, and I shall follow on. When you hear a noise like a clap of thunder, don't be afraid. If people ask, tell them: 'That's my little frog arriving in her little carriage.'"

So Ivan-Tsarevich went off to the banquet alone. His elder brothers came with their wives who were dressed in fine clothes and jewels with their cheeks rouged and their eyebrows darkened. They stood and laughed at Ivan-Tsarevich:

"Why have you not come with your wife? You could at least have brought her in a handkerchief. Where did you find such a beauty? You must have scoured the whole marsh!"

The Tsar, his sons, the two brides, and the invited guests sat down to dine at oak tables covered with finely-patterned table-cloths. Suddenly there was a noise like a clap of thunder. The guests took fright and sprang from their chairs, but Ivan-Tsarevich called out:

"Do not be alarmed, dear guests: It's my little frog arriving in her little carriage."

A golden carriage drawn by six white horses sped up to the Tsar's porch and out got Vasilisa the Wise. Wearing a sky-blue dress spangled with stars and a glittering tiara in her hair, she was more beautiful than can be imagined or described. She took Ivan-Tsarevich by the hand and allowed herself to be led to the oak tables with their finely-patterned table-cloths.

The guests began to eat, drink and enjoy themselves. Vasilisa the Wise drank from a glass and poured the last drops into her left sleeve. She ate some roast swan and tucked the bones into her right sleeve.

The other royal brides saw what she was doing and decided to copy her.

After the feasting was over, the time came to dance. Vasilisa the Wise took Ivan-Tsarevich and led him onto the floor. She tripped and turned, turned and tripped in such a way that everyone was astonished. Then she swung her left arm and a lake appeared; she swung her right and there were white swans swimming on the lake. The Tsar and his guests were amazed.

The other brides then got up to dance. They swung their left arms and only splashed the guests; they swung their right arms and scattered bones everywhere. One of the bones struck the Tsar in the eye and he was so furious he sent them both from the hall.

Meanwhile Ivan-Tsarevich had himself crept from the hall. He ran home and there he found the frog's skin. He threw it into the stove and watched as it burnt up.

When Vasilisa the Wise came home she was horrified not to find her frog's skin. She sat down on a bench, shaking her head in despair, and said to her husband:

"Oh, Ivan-Tsarevich, what have you done! You had only to wait three more days and I would have been yours for ever. Now I have to bid you farewell. You must seek me at the other end of the world, where I shall be in the power of Kashchéi the Immortal."

With that Vasilisa the Wise turned into a grey cuckoo and flew out of the window. Ivan-Tsarevich wept and wept, then he took his leave and set off he knew not where to seek his wife. He walked and walked until his boots were worn through, his caftan was threadbare and the rain had ruined his hat.

Then an old, old man crossed his path:

"Greetings, young sir! What are you seeking? Whither are you bound?"

Ivan-Tsarevich told him about his misfortune and the old, old man told him:

"Oh, Ivan-Tsarevich, why did you burn the frog's skin? You did not put it on her and it was not for you to take it off. Vasilisa the Wise was born cleverer than her father. He grew angry with her for that reason and ordered her to spend three years as a frog. Well, there's nothing more to be done. Here, take this ball of yarn. Follow it boldly wherever it rolls."

Ivan-Tsarevich thanked the old, old man and set off after the ball of yarn. The ball kept rolling and he followed it.

Once in the open countryside he came across a bear. Ivan-Tsarevich took aim and was about to kill the bear when it spoke to him in a human voice:

"Don't kill me, Ivan-Tsarevich. I shall be of use to you."

Ivan-Tsarevich dropped his bow and spared the bear.

He walked on and, glancing up, saw a drake flying past. He took aim, but the drake spoke to him in a human voice:

"Don't kill me, Ivan-Tsarevich. I shall be of use to you."

Ivan-Tsarevich spared the drake and walked on.

A hare ran across his path. Again Ivan-Tsarevich snatched up his bow and was about to shoot when the hare spoke to him in a human voice:

"Don't kill me, Ivan-Tsarevich. I shall be of use to you."

He spared the hare and walked on. He came to the deep blue sea and there on the sand he saw a pike. It was barely breathing and gasped out:

"Ivan-Tsarevich, spare me! Throw me back into the deep blue sea!"

He tossed the pike back into the sea and walked on along the shore.

After a time, the ball of yarn brought him to a forest. There he found a hut on chicken's legs, turning around. Ivan-Tsarevich called out:

"Hut, o hut, stand as your mother placed you of old: your back to the trees, your front to me!"

The hut turned so that its back was to the trees and its front to Ivan-Tsarevich. He climbed inside and there on the stove, on the ninth brick, he saw Bába-Yagá with her leg of bone. Her teeth were on the shelf and her nose had grown into the ceiling.

"Why have you come calling, my fine young man?" Baba-Yaga asked him. "Are you seeking an adventure, or seeking to avoid one?"

But Ivan-Tsarevich replied:

"You old hag, you should give me food and drink and let me use the bathhouse before you start your questioning."

Baba-Yaga let him use the bathhouse, gave him food and drink and made him up a bed. Then Ivan-Tsarevich told her that he was looking for his wife, Vasilisa the Wise.

"I know, I know," Baba-Yaga said. "Your wife is now in the power of Kashchei the Immortal. It will be no easy matter to recover her, as Kashchei is hard to deal with. His death is at the tip of a needle; that needle is in an egg; that egg is in a duck; that duck is in a hare; that hare sits in a stone box; that stone box rests in a tall oak; and Kashchei guards that oak with all his might."

Ivan-Tsarevich spent the night in Baba-Yaga's hut and in the morning she pointed out to him the place where the tall oak grew. He set off walking and at last he came to the oak. He looked up and sure enough there in its branches was a stone box, way out of reach.

Suddenly, from out of nowhere, a bear ran up and tore the oak out by the roots. The stone box fell down and broke open. Out sprang a hare and ran off as fast as its legs could carry it. But another hare went chasing after it, caught it and tore it to pieces. Out flew a duck and climbed way up into the sky. But a drake dived onto the duck and struck it so hard that it dropped the egg. The egg fell into the deep blue sea...

At that moment Ivan-Tsarevich burst into tears — how could he hope to find the egg in the sea? Suddenly the pike swam in to shore with the egg in its mouth. Ivan-Tsarevich took the egg, broke it, pulled out the needle and began with all his strength to snap off the tip. He strained and strained, and Kashchei the Immortal writhed and dashed about. For all Kashchei's struggling, Ivan-Tsarevich managed to break the tip of the needle and Kashchei had to die.

Ivan-Tsarevich went into Kashchei's palace of white stone and Vasilisa the Wise came running out to meet him. She kissed him on his sweet lips. Ivan-Tsarevich and Vasilisa the Wise returned home where both they lived happily to a ripe old age.

Masha and the Bear

Once upon a time there was an old man and woman who lived in a village together with their little granddaughter named Masha. One day the village girls decided to go into the forest to gather berries and mushrooms. They came and asked Masha to join them.

"Grandfather, grandmother," Masha said, "may I go into the forest with the village girls?"

And the old couple replied:

"Yes, you may, only be sure to stay with the others and don't get lost."

The girls went into the forest and began gathering berries and mushrooms. Little Masha went from tree to tree and from bush to bush, and before long she had wandered far away from the others. She looked for them and shouted their names, but they could not hear her and did not reply. Little Masha kept walking through the forest, first this way, then that, and became thoroughly lost. She came right to the heart of the forest, to the densest part, and there stood a little wooden house. Masha knocked on the door, but there was no reply. She pushed on the door, and it opened. Little Masha went into the wooden house. She sat down on a bench by the window. As she sat, she thought:

"Who might live here? Why is no-one home?"

The house belonged to a great big bear. He was not at home just then, because he was walking in the forest. In the evening the bear came back. He saw little Masha and was delighted.

"Oho," he said, "now I shall keep you here! You will live in my house, feed the stove, make porridge and serve it to me."

Now Masha was very unhappy at this idea. She cried for a long time, but she had no choice. And so she began to live in the bear's wooden house.

The bear would go out into the forest for the whole day, telling Masha not to leave the house while he was away.

"Even if you do go off," he said, "I shall soon find you — and then I shall eat you!"

Little Masha began to think how she could get away from the bear. There was dense forest all around; she did not know which way to go, and there was no-one to ask. She thought and thought, and came up with an idea. Once, when the bear came back from walking in the forest, Masha said to him:

"Bear, let me go back to the village for a day. I shall bake some pies and take them to grandmother and grandfather."

"No, no," said the bear; "you will lose your way in the forest. Give me the pies and I shall take them myself."

And that was just what Masha wanted!

She baked the pies, put them in a dish, took down a huge pannier — a kind of basket you wear on your back — and said to the bear:

"Look, I shall put the pies in this basket for you to take to grandmother and grandfather. Only promise not to open the basket on the way and take out the pies. I shall climb to the top of that great oak and watch you."

"Very well," the bear replied, "give me the basket."

Then Masha said:

"Just go out on the porch and take a look whether it is raining, would you."

As soon as the bear was outside, Masha leapt into the pannier and pulled the dish of pies in on top of her. The bear came in and saw that the basket was ready. He swung it onto his back and set off for the village. The bear wandered past firs. He wandered past birches. Uphill and downhill he went, until he felt tired and said out loud:

> "I'll just take the weight off my feet
> And have a little pie to eat!"

But Masha called out from the basket:

> "I can see you! I can see you!
> Don't take the weight off your feet!
> Don't have a little pie to eat!
> Take them to grandmother!
> Take them to grandfather!"

"What eyesight she must have," the bear said. "She can see everything."

He lifted the pannier and kept walking. He walked and walked until he felt really tired. Then he stopped, sat down and said:

> "I'll just take the weight off my feet
> And have a little pie to eat!"

But again Masha called out from the basket:

> "I can see you! I can see you!
> Don't take the weight off your feet!
> Don't have a little pie to eat!
> Take them to grandmother!
> Take them to grandfather!"

The bear was astonished:

"You can't outsmart her! She must have climbed way up high to see this far!"

He reached the village, found the house where Masha's grandparents lived and knocked on the gate as hard as he could. Knock, knock.

"Open up, open up! I've brought you pies from little Masha."

But the village dogs caught the scent of the bear and came barking and running from every yard. The bear took fright, left the pannier by the gate and hurried back to the forest without looking round. At that moment Masha's grandparents came out to the gate. They looked and saw only the big basket.

"What can be in this basket?" the old woman asked.

The old man lifted the lid and simply stared. He could not believe his eyes — there in the pannier sat Masha, whom they had given up for lost, alive and well. Grandmother and grandfather were delighted. They hugged and kissed Masha and praised her for outwitting the bear.

 # The Speckled Hen

An old couple lived way back when, whose greatest joy was a speckled hen.
Now that hen an egg did lay, bright and shiny, not dark, nor grey.
To keep that egg safe and sound, she put it in a hollow she had found,
But a passing mouse, half-awake, chanced that splendid egg to break.
The sight made Grandpa start to cry and Grandma begin to weep.
The chickens fluttered into the sky and the gates began to creak.
The doors grew warped; the fence did fall; the roof stirred and groaned above it all.
But just then the speckled hen in her loudest voice called out to them.
> "Grandpa don't cry; Grandma don't weep.
> Chickens don't flutter; gates don't creak.
> Doors don't warp; fence don't fall.
> Roof stay still above us all.
> Keep quiet, keep calm," she cajoled.
> "Another egg for you I'll lay,
> Bright and shiny, not dark, nor grey,
> Not commonplace – but made of gold."

The Cockerel
with the Golden Crest

Once upon a time there were a cat, a thrush and a cockerel with a golden crest, who all lived together in a little wooden house in the forest.

One day the cat and the thrush went out to cut firewood, leaving the cockerel on his own. As they left, they warned him: "We are going far away and you will be here alone looking after the house. When the cunning fox comes past, be sure the window stays shut fast."

The fox soon found out that the cat and the thrush were not at home. He ran to the wooden house, sat down under the window and sang out:

>O cockerel with your golden crest,
>Beautiful hackles and silky breast,
>Open the window, won't you please,
>And I shall give you your fill of peas.

When he heard that, the cockerel put his head out of the window. Quick as a flash the fox grabbed him and hurried away home. The frightened cockerel called out:

>The fox is carrying me to his lair
>Through forests dark and mountains bare
>Over rivers that flow fast and free.
>Come cat, come thrush, and rescue me!

The cat and the thrush heard him, dashed after the fox and managed to get the cockerel away from him.

When the time came for the cat and the thrush to go into the forest again for firewood, they told the cockerel: "This time be sure not to look out of the window, as we are going even farther away and will not hear you if you call."

They went off and soon the fox again appeared beneath the window and sang:

>O cockerel with your golden crest,
>Beautiful hackles and silky breast,
>Open the window, won't you please,
>And I shall give you your fill of peas.

The cockerel kept quiet and still, so the fox went on:

>The children came merrily,
>Scattering the corn about.
>The hens they eat it greedily,
>But cockerels must go without.

At that the cockerel stuck his head out of the window and cackled:

"What, what, what? What do you mean 'go without'?" The fox grabbed him and hurried away home. The frightened cockerel called out:

> The fox is carrying me to his lair
> Through forests dark and mountains bare
> Over rivers that flow fast and free.
> Come cat, come thrush, and rescue me!

The cat and the thrush heard him and dashed after the fox. The cat ran as fast as he could; the thrush flew swiftly above the wood. They caught up with the fox. The thrush fluttered and pecked; the cat scratched and bit to good effect — and they got the cockerel away.

After some time the cat and the thrush had to go into the forest for firewood again. As they left they warned the cockerel as strongly as they could: "Do not listen to the fox. Do not look out of the window. We are going even farther and will not hear if you call."

Off they went into the forest. As soon as they had gone, the fox was back. He sat beneath the window and sang:

> O cockerel with your golden crest,
> Beautiful hackles and silky breast,
> Open the window, won't you please,
> And I shall give you your fill of peas.

The cockerel kept quiet and still, so the fox went on:

> The children came merrily,
> Scattering the corn about.
> The hens they eat it greedily,
> But cockerels must go without.

Still the cockerel kept quiet, so the fox went on:

> People too came merrily
> Scattering tasty nuts about
> The hens they eat them happily,
> But cockerels must go without.

At that the cockerel stuck his head out of the window and cackled: "What, what, what? What do you mean 'go without'?" The fox grabbed him tight and hurried through forests dark and mountains bare, over rivers that flow fast and free, all the way to his lair.

The frightened cockerel called and called, but all in vain. The cat and the thrush did not hear him and it was only

when they returned home that they found he was gone.

The pair hurried after the fox. The cat ran as fast as he could, the thrush flew swiftly above the wood... and they came to the fox's lair. The cat took his gúsli — a stringed instrument a bit like a zither— and began to play:

Hum, gusli, sing,
String upon silver string.
Here is the fox's cosy lair.
I wonder, will we find him there?

The fox listened and thought to himself: "I'll just take a peek to see who is playing so well and singing so sweetly."

He climbed out of his lair and the cat and the thrush pounced on him. They fluttered and bit, scratched and pecked until he gave up and ran away.

They found the cockerel, sat him in a basket and carried him back home.

The three of them never had any more trouble from the fox and they are still living happily together to this day.

Yelena the Wise

Once upon a time, in a country far away, there was a soldier whose duty it was to stand guard at a stone tower. This tower was kept locked up and had a great seal on the door as well. One night, exactly at midnight, the soldier heard someone calling to him from the tower.

"Hey, soldier!"

The soldier replied, "Who's that calling me?"

"It's me, a poor imp," answered a voice from behind the iron grille. "I have been locked up here thirty years without food nor drink."

"What do you want?"

"Let me out of here. When you are in need, I shall help you. You have only to mention me, and I shall be right there by your side."

The soldier straightaway tore off the great seal, broke the lock and prised open the door. The imp flew out of the tower, soared into the air and disappeared faster than lightning.

"Well," thought the soldier, "now I've done it: all my years of service will count for nothing. Now I'll be arrested and brought before a court martial. They'll likely make me run the gauntlet – through all the ranks while the other soldiers beat me. No, I'd better run away, while there's still time."

He dropped his gun and knapsack on the ground and took off as fast as he could. He walked all the next day, and the next, and the third. He was terribly hungry, but had nothing to eat or drink. At last he sat down by the roadside, weeping bitter tears, and thought to himself:

"How stupid I am. I served the tsar for ten years. I was always happy and well fed. I got three pounds of bread every day. But, no! I had to go and run off, so as to die of hunger. Hey, imp, it's all your fault!"

Suddenly, out of nowhere, the imp appeared and said, "Greetings, soldier! Why so sad?"

"Of course, I am sad, when I haven't had a bite to eat for three days."

"Well, that's easily put right," said the imp. He dashed here and there and brought all sorts of wines and victuals. The soldier ate and drank his fill; then the imp invited him to go back with him.

"In my home you shall live at ease: drink, eat and enjoy yourself as much as you like. Only keep an eye on my daughters – that's all you need to do."

The soldier agreed. The imp took him by the arm, carried him high into the air and took him far, far away to a palace made of white stone. The imp had three daughters, each of them a great beauty. He told them to obey the soldier and to give him whatever he liked to eat and drink; then he flew off to do some more mischief – he was an imp after all. He never sat still, but was always going about the world disturbing people and encouraging them to sin.

The soldier was left behind with the beautiful maidens, to live in such comfort that he had no need of heaven. Only one thing bothered him: every night the three beauties would leave the palace and go somewhere, but where he did not know. When he asked them about it, they avoided his questions and would say nothing.

"Very well," the soldier thought, "I shall keep watch all night and find out where you get to."

That evening the soldier went to bed and pretended to be fast asleep, but inside he was burning with excitement to see what would happen.

When the time came he quietly crept to the girls' bedroom, stopped by the door and knelt down to look through the keyhole. The beautiful maidens took out a magic carpet and spread it on the floor. They each stamped on the carpet and turned into doves, spread their wings and flew out of the window.

"How wonderful!" the soldier thought. "I'll try that myself."

He opened the door to the bedroom, jumped on the carpet and turned into a robin redbreast. The robin flew out of the window and after the others. The doves came down on a green meadow, and the robin settled beneath a currant bush where he could watch hidden by the leaves. Huge numbers of doves flew down to that same spot. They covered the whole meadow, apart from the golden throne that stood in the middle. After a short while the sky and earth were lit up as a golden chariot drawn by six fiery dragons came flying through the air. In the chariot sat Yelena the Wise – more beautiful than can be imagined or guessed or even described in a fairy tale. She climbed out of her chariot and sat on the golden throne. She called the doves to her one by one and began to teach them various pieces of wisdom. When she was done teaching she climbed into her chariot and was gone. At that every single dove took off from the green meadow and each flew its own way home. The robin redbreast flew after the three sisters and ended up in the bedroom with them. The doves struck the carpet and turned back into beautiful maidens; the robin did the same and turned back into the soldier.

"Where did you come from?" the girls asked.

"Aha! I was with you at the green meadow, saw the beautiful princess on the golden throne and heard her teaching you all sorts of cunning things."

"Well you are lucky to be able to tell the tale. For that princess is Yelena the Wise, our mighty ruler. If she had had her magic book with her, she would have recognised you at once and a cruel death would have been your lot. Have a care, soldier! Fly no more to the green meadow to gaze upon Yelena the Wise, or else you will lose that hot head of yours."

The soldier was not downhearted. All their words went in one ear and out of the other. When night came, he again struck the carpet and turned into a robin redbreast. The robin flew to the green meadow, hid beneath the currant bush and watched Yelena the Wise. He admired her untold beauty and thought to himself, "If I could have a wife like that, I could wish for nothing more in this world. I shall fly after her and find out where she lives."

So Yelena the Wise got off her golden throne, climbed into her chariot and soared through the air to her marvellous palace. And behind her flew the little robin.

The princess reached the palace. Her nurses and nannies ran out to meet her, took her by the arms and led her into the finely painted chambers. Meanwhile the robin flew around the garden. He chose a fine-looking tree that happened to stand beneath the princess's bedroom, and perched on one of its branches. He began to sing so well and so sorrowfully that the princess did not sleep a wink – she just had to keep listening.

As soon as the sun came up, Yelena the Wise called out in a loud voice, "Nurses and nannies, be quick and run into the garden! Catch that robin redbreast for me!"

The nurses and nannies dashed into the garden and began trying to catch the songbird. But what could the old dears do? The robin hopped from bush to bush, never flying far away, but always out of reach.

The princess lost her patience. She ran out into the garden to catch the robin herself. She approached the bush where the bird was sitting. The bird never stirred, sitting with its wings folded as if waiting for her.

The princess was delighted. She picked up the little bird and took it into the palace. She put it into a golden cage that she hung in her bedroom.

The day passed and the sun started setting. Yelena the Wise flew to the green meadow and returned. She started taking off her robes, undressed and got into bed. The robin looked at her white body, at her untold beauty and trembled all over. As soon as the princess fell asleep, the robin turned into a fly and flew out of the golden cage. He struck the floor and turned into a fine figure of a man.

This fine figure of a man went up to the princess's bed and stared and stared at her beauty. At last he could not resist any longer and planted a kiss on her sweet lips. The princess began to wake up. He quickly turned back into a fly, slipped between the bars of the cage and became a robin.

Yelena the Wise opened her eyes. She looked all around, but there was no-one to be seen. "I must have been dreaming," she said to herself, turned over and went back to sleep.

The soldier couldn't help himself. He did the same thing a second time and a third, but each time he kissed her she woke up.

The third time she got out of bed and said, "There is something more to this. Let me take a look in my magic book."

She looked in her magic book and immediately discovered that sitting in the golden cage was not a simple robin, but a young soldier.

"Oh you bold villain!" shouted Yelena the Wise. "Come out of the cage. You shall pay for your deceit with your life."

There was nothing for it. The robin redbreast flew out of the cage, struck the floor and turned into a fine figure of a man. The soldier fell on his knees before the princess and began begging forgiveness.

"No mercy for you, you villain," said Yelena the Wise and called for the executioner and his block to have the soldier beheaded.

From out of nowhere a great giant appeared with an axe and a block. He pushed the soldier to the floor, pressed his hot head to the block and raised the axe. The princess had only to wave her handkerchief and the young fellow's head would fly from his shoulders.

"Have pity, beautiful princess," the soldier begged through his tears. "Let me sing one last time."

"Sing, then, but be quick about it!"

The soldier launched into such a sad, mournful song that Yelena the Wise herself burst into tears. She felt sorry for the young fellow and said to the soldier,

"I shall give you ten hours. If in that time you manage to conceal yourself so cunningly that I cannot find you, then I shall marry you. If not, then I shall have your head cut from your shoulders."

The soldier left the palace. He wandered into a thick forest and sat down under a bush. He thought and thought, then suddenly cried out, "Oh, imp! All my troubles are because of you!"

That very instant the imp appeared.

"What is your wish, soldier?"

"Listen," said the soldier. "I am about to be killed. Where can I hide from Yelena the Wise?"

The imp struck the damp earth and turned into a great grey-winged eagle.

"Climb on my back, soldier, and I shall carry you into the heavens."

The soldier climbed onto the eagle. The great bird soared upwards and rose above the dark clouds.

Five hours passed and Yelena the Wise took up her magic book. She looked in it and saw everything clearly. She called out in a great loud voice, "That's enough flying into the heavens, eagle. Come down to earth, you cannot hide from me anyway."

The eagle flew back down.

The soldier was even more distraught.

"What can I do now? Where can I hide?"

"Wait," said the imp, "I'll help you."

He hopped up to the soldier, struck him on the cheek and turned him into a pin. He turned himself into a little mouse, snatched up the pin in his teeth, crept into the palace, found the magic book and stuck the pin into it.

Another five hours passed. Yelena the Wise opened her magic book and pored over it. But the book showed her nothing. The princess grew very angry and flung it into the stove. The pin slipped from the book, struck the floor and turned into a fine young fellow.

Yelena the Wise took him by the hand and said, "I am cunning, but you are more cunning still."

Without further ado the pair were married and lived happily ever after.

Ivashko and Baba-Yaga

Once upon a time there was an old childless couple who lived in the country-side. One day in wintertime the old man went into the forest for firewood. He chopped as much wood as they needed and also cut down a young lime-tree that had been stripped of its bark. When he came home he stacked the firewood in the yard, but carried the lime log into the house and put it under the stove. On the third day there was a shuffling noise from under the stove and then a voice called out:

"Father! Mother! Take me out!"

The old couple took fright. Then they heard the voice again:

"Father! Mother! Take me out!"

The old man looked beneath the stove and there he saw a little boy. He pulled him out and showed him to his wife. They decided to call him Ivashko – Little Ivan – and gave him food and drink.

When summer came the boy started to catch fish and in that way he was able to feed and support the old man and woman.

Sometimes the old woman would come down to the lake where he was fishing and call out to him, "Ivashko, Ivashko, Ivashko! Come in to the shore and I'll give you some tasty pie to eat." As soon as he heard his mother's voice, Ivashko would pull in to the shore, take the piece of pie from her and give her the fish he had caught.

Once Baba-Yaga happened to witness this scene. She bided her time then came down to the same spot and began to call Ivashko in with the same words his mother had used. But Ivashko heard Baba-Yaga's thick voice and called back, "That's not mother's voice. It's far too thick. Go and sharpen your tongue!"

And Baba-Yaga went away disappointed. Later the old woman that he called mother came down to lake and began to call him, "Ivashko, Ivashko, Ivashko! Come in to the shore and I'll give you some tasty pie to eat."

Ivashko heard his mother's voice, pulled in to the shore, took the pie from her and gave her the fish he had caught.

The old woman went off. Meanwhile Baba-Yaga had sharpened her tongue on a grindstone and after waiting a while went down to the shore and began beckoning to Ivashko. The boy failed to recognize her voice, thought it was his mother calling and pulled in to the shore. Baba-Yaga grabbed him and carried him off to her hut.

Now Baba-Yaga had three daughters. She told the eldest daughter to stoke up the stove as hot as hot could be, so as to cook young Ivashko, while she herself went out for a walk. The eldest daughter stoked the stove, then took Ivashko and told him to sit on the baking shovel. Ivashko was not stupid and began to make excuses, saying that he didn't know how to sit on the shovel.

"I'm not sure," he said, "show me how to do it."

Baba-Yaga's daughter sat on the shovel and Ivashko quickly grabbed hold of the handle and popped her into the stove. He himself climbed into the loft.

Baba-Yaga came back and asked for Ivashko. The other two daughters pulled their sister out of the stove and served her to their mother, who ate her up. She went out into the yard and said, "I'm rolling and rocking on Ivashko's bones!"

Ivashko, sitting up in the loft, said to himself, "You're rolling and rocking on your daughter's bones!"

Baba-Yaga caught sight of Ivashko and shouted, "I'm coming up to get you, Ivashko!"

She grabbed the boy and gave him to her daughters with orders to roast him, while she went for another walk. The daughters stoked up the stove again. The middle daughter wanted to put Ivashko on the shovel, but he tricked her too and popped her in the stove. Then he did the same with the youngest. Baba-Yaga came home and called her daughters, but nobody answered. She herself took the roast out of the stove and ate it up. Then she went out into the yard and said, "I'm rolling and rocking on Ivashko's bones!"

But Ivashko, shouted down from the loft, "You're rolling and rocking on your daughters' bones, you old fool!"

Baba-Yaga spotted him and tried furiously to catch him. Ivashko shouted out in a mournful voice, "Hey, swans, swans, geese, my dears! Fly down and each spare a feather for me."

The swan-geese flew down; each of them pulled out a feather. They made a pair of wings and gave them to Ivashko. Ivashko put them on and flew away from Baba-Yaga back to his father and mother. With them he lived long and well, and caught more fish than I can tell.

Vasilisa the Beautiful

Once in a land far away there lived a merchant. He was married for twelve years, but the couple had only one daughter, Vasilisa the Beautiful. When her mother died, the girl was eight years old. On her death-bed the merchant's wife called her daughter to her. She took a little doll from under the blanket, gave it to the girl and said, "Listen, my dear Vasilisa. Remember my last words and do as I say. I am dying and together with a mother's blessing I leave you this doll. Keep her with you always, but show her to no-one. When some misfortune befalls you, give her something to eat and ask her advice. She will eat and tell you what to do."

Then the mother kissed her daughter and passed away. After her death the merchant mourned as is proper, but then he began to think of marrying again. He was a good man and there was no shortage of would-be brides, but the one he liked the most was a certain widow. She was no longer young and had two daughters of her own almost the same age as Vasilisa – a good housekeeper and an experienced mother, then. The merchant married the widow, but she did not become a kind second mother to Vasilisa as he had hoped. Vasilisa was the most beautiful girl in the whole village. Her step-mother and step-sisters envied her looks and gave her all sorts of impossible tasks to make her lose flesh from overwork and to make her lily-white skin turn brown from the wind and sun. Her life became a torment.

Vasilisa bore everything meekly and her looks and figure grew finer with every passing day. Her step-mother and her daughters on the other hand lost weight from malice and grew ugly from wickedness, although they did nothing all day like the grandest ladies. How did that come about? Well Vasilisa was helped by her little doll. How else could the poor girl have managed all the work? At times, though, Vasilisa would not eat herself, saving some tasty titbit for the doll and late in the evening, when everyone had gone to bed, she locked herself in the store-room, where she lived, and fed her.

"Here you are, little doll, eat well and hear the sad tale I have to tell. Though I still live in my father's house I know no joy, my wicked step-mother is working me to death. Teach me what to do and how to act."

The little doll ate and then gave her advice. She comforted the poor girl and in the morning she did all sorts of work for her. Vasilisa rested in the shade and picked flowers, while the beds were weeded, the cabbage watered, the water brought from the well and the stove heated. The little doll also showed Vasilisa a herb to protect her lily-white skin. With her doll to help her, life was good.

The years went by and Vasilisa became of an age to marry. All the young men of the village sought her hand, and none of them spared a second glance for her step-sisters. The step-mother grew even nastier and told all the suitors,

"The younger girl shall not marry before the older ones are wed."

And when she had sent the suitors on their way, she took her anger out on Vasilisa.

It so happened that the merchant had to go away on business for a long time. The step-mother took this chance to move the family to another house that stood by a dense forest. In a clearing in that forest stood a hut and in that hut lived Baba-Yaga. She never let anyone into her home and ate people like you eat roast chicken. Once they had moved, the merchant's wife would send Vasilisa, whom she hated, into the forest every now and again on some excuse, but the girl always returned safe and sound. The little doll showed her the path and kept her away from Baba-Yaga's hut.

Autumn came around. The step-mother gave all three girls work to do in the evenings: one had to make lace, another knit stockings, while Vasilisa had to spin. She put out the lights all over the house, leaving only one candle where the girls were working, and retired to bed. The girls kept working. The candle began to gutter. One of the step-sisters took tongs to trim the wick, but instead – as her mother had told her – she put the candle out as if by accident.

"What are we to do now?" said the girls. "There's no light in the whole house and we still haven't finished our tasks. Someone must go and fetch a light from Baba-Yaga"

"My pins give me light enough," said the one who was making lace. "I'll not go!"

"And I'll not go either," said the one who was knitting stockings. "My pins give me light enough too!"

"You should go for a light!" the pair shouted. "Get off to Baba-Yaga!" And they pushed Vasilisa out of the room.

Vasilisa went to her store-room, put what she had saved from supper before the little doll and said, "Here you are, little doll, eat well and hear the sad tale I have to tell. I am being sent to Baba-Yaga for a light. Baba-Yaga will eat me!"

The doll ate and her eyes flared up like two candles.

"Fear not, dear Vasilisa," she said. "Go where you are sent; only keep me always by you. While I am near, Baba-Yaga will do nothing to you."

Vasilisa got ready to go out. She put the little doll in her pocket and, crossing herself, went into the thick forest. She trembled as she walked. Suddenly a horseman galloped past: he was white himself, dressed in white, and mounted on a white horse with a white harness. It began to grow light. She walked on and another horseman galloped by. This one was red himself, dressed in red, and mounted on a red horse. The sun began to rise.

Vasilisa walked for a whole night and day. Only towards evening did she come to the clearing where Baba-Yaga's hut stood. Around the hut was a fence of human bones and stuck on the fence were human skulls with eyes. Instead of gateposts there were human legs, instead of bolts arms and instead of a lock a mouth with sharp teeth. Vasilisa stood frozen to the spot with fear. Suddenly another horseman appeared: he was black himself, dressed in black, and mounted on a black horse. He rode up to Baba-Yaga's gate and disappeared without a trace. Night fell. But the darkness did not last long: the eyes of all the skulls on the fence lit up and the whole clearing became as bright as day. Vasilisa trembled with fear, but as she did not know where to run, she stayed put.

Soon a terrible noise could be heard in the forest: the trees cracked, the dry leaves rustled and Baba-Yaga came out of the forest. She was riding in a great mortar, driving it on with a pestle and sweeping her trail with a broom. She drove up to the gates and stopped. She sniffed the air and shouted out, "Fie, fie! I smell a Russian soul! Who's here?"

Terrified, Vasilisa approached the old woman and, bowing low, said, "It is me, granny! My step-mother's daughters have sent me to you for a light."

"Very well," said Baba-Yaga. "I know them. Stay with me a while and do some work, then I shall give you a light. If not, I shall eat you!"

Then she turned to the gates and shouted out:

"Hey, my strong bolts, fly back. My broad gates, fly open!"

The gates opened and Baba-Yaga drove in whistling. Vasilisa followed her and everything shut up again behind her.

Going inside, Baba-Yaga stretched herself and said to Vasilisa, "Serve me what there is there in the stove. I am hungry."

Vasilisa lit a spill from one of the skulls on the fence and began to take the food out of the stove and serve it to Baba-Yaga. There was enough there to feed about ten people. From the cellar she brought kvass, mead, beer and wine. And the old woman ate and drank it all. Vasilisa kept back only a little cabbage soup, a crust of bread and a slice of suckling pig.

After that Baba-Yaga went to bed, saying, "When I go off tomorrow, you must clean the yard, sweep the house, prepare a meal, do the laundry and go to the corn-bin, take twenty bushels of wheat and pick all the fennel seeds from it. And if you don't do all of that, I shall eat you."

After giving her orders, Baba-Yaga began snoring. Vasilisa put the leftovers of the meal in front of doll, burst into tears and whispered, "Here you are, little doll, eat well and hear the sad tale I have to tell. Baba-Yaga has given me hard work to do and threatens to eat me if I fail. Help me."

The doll replied, "Fear not, Vasilisa the Beautiful. Eat, say your prayers and go to bed. Things will look better in the morning."

Vasilisa awoke very early, but Baba-Yaga was already up. She looked out of the window and the eyes of the skulls were beginning to fade. The white horseman passed by and day began to break. Baba-Yaga went out into the yard and whistled. Her mortar, pestle and broom immediately appeared.

The red horseman passed by and the sun rose. Baba-Yaga got into the mortar and left the yard, driving with the pestle and sweeping her trail with the broom. Vasilisa was left alone. She looked over Baba-Yaga's house and was amazed at the abundance of everything. She paused uncertain which task to tackle first. She looked again and all the work was done; the little doll was just taking the last fennel seeds from the wheat.

"Oh my deliverer," said Vasilisa to the doll. "You have saved me from misfortune!"

"All you have to do is to cook a meal," the doll replied as she climbed back into Vasilisa's pocket. "God speed your cooking, then you can rest."

By evening Vasilisa had laid the table and was waiting for Baba-Yaga. Twilight came and the black horseman passed by the gates. Dark night came on. Only the eyes of the skulls gave light. The trees cracked, the dry leaves rustled and Baba-Yaga came back. Vasilisa went out to meet her.

"Have you done everything?" asked Baba-Yaga.

"See for yourself, granny," said Vasilisa.

Baba-Yaga looked everything over, disappointed that she had no cause for complaint, and said, "Very well, then."

Then she shouted out, "My loyal servants, my dear friends, grind my wheat!"

Three pairs of hands appeared, grasped the grain and carried it out of sight. Baba-Yaga ate her fill and on her way to bed gave Vasilisa more orders.

"Tomorrow you must do the same as today and as well as that take the poppy-seed from the store and clean it of earth down to the last grain, because someone mixed it with soil out of spite."

When she finished speaking the old woman turned her face to the wall and began snoring. Vasilisa set about feeding her doll. The doll ate and said to her as before,

"Say your prayers and go to bed. Things will look better in the morning. Everything will be done, dear Vasilisa."

In the morning Baba-Yaga again rode out of the yard in her mortar and with the doll's help Vasilisa managed all the work straight away. The old woman came back, looked everything over and shouted, "My loyal servants, my dear friends, press oil from my poppy-seed."

Three pairs of hands appeared, grasped the poppy-seed and carried it out of sight. Baba-Yaga sat down to eat. While she ate, Vasilisa stood in silence.

"Why don't you say anything to me?" asked Baba-Yaga. "You stand there as if you're dumb."

"I didn't dare," said Vasilisa, "but if you'll allow there is one thing I should like to ask about."

"Ask away. Only not every question brings a good outcome. If you know a lot, you'll soon grow old."

"I only want to ask you, granny, about what I saw. As I was coming to you, I was passed by a man on a white horse who was all white and dressed in white. Who was it?"

"That's my bright day," Baba-Yaga replied.

"And what is the meaning of the black horseman who overtook me right at your gates?"

"That is my black night. They are all my loyal servants."

Vasilisa remembered the three pairs of hands, but said nothing.

"Why don't you ask anything else?" inquired Baba-Yaga.

"That's enough for me, granny. Why, you yourself said that if you know a lot, you'll soon grow old."

"It's good," said Baba-Yaga, "that you ask only about what you saw beyond the fence and not inside! I do not like it when people mind my business and when they get too nosy I eat them! Now I have a question for you: how do you manage to do all the tasks that I set you?"

"I am helped by my mother's blessing," Vasilisa replied.

"So that's the way of it. Get out of my sight, blessed daughter! I don't need the blessed."

She dragged Vasilisa outside and pushed her through the gate. But she took one of the skulls with burning eyes from the fence and, impaling it on a stick, gave it to the girl, saying, "Here's your light for your step-mother's daughters. Take it. That's what you were sent here for."

Vasilisa set off at a run by the light from the skull that faded only when morning came. At last, by the evening of that next day she reached her home.

As she approached the gates, she wanted to get rid off the skull. "That's right," she thought to herself, "they don't need light any more." But suddenly she heard a muffled voice from the skull.

"Don't leave me. Take me to you step-mother."

She looked at her step-mother's house and, as she could not see a light in any of the windows, she decided to take the skull in with her. For the first time she was welcomed with kindness. They told her that since she had left there had been neither light nor fire in the house. They had been unable to strike a light themselves and any they brought from the neighbours went out as soon as it crossed the threshold.

"Perhaps your light will hold," said her step-mother. They carried the skull into the house and its eyes looked so hard at the step-mother and her daughters that they burnt. They tried to hide, but wherever they dashed those terrible eyes kept following them. By morning they had been burnt to cinders. Only Vasilisa was left untouched.

In the morning Vasilisa buried the skull, locked up the house and went into town. She asked an old woman with no family whether she could live with her. She lived quietly awaiting her father's return. One day she said to the old woman, "I'm bored with nothing to do, granny. Go and buy me some flax of the finest sort and I shall spin it."

The old woman bought the flax and Vasilisa sat down to work. She worked so well that the yarn came out even and thin as a hair. She made a lot of yarn and the time came to weave it into cloth. But they couldn't find a reed fine enough to use on Vasilisa's yarn and no-one would undertake to make one. (The reed is the piece of the loom that looks a bit like a comb and presses the cloth tightly together.)

Vasilisa consulted her doll, who said, "Find me any old reed and an old shuttle and a horse's mane and I shall make all you need."

Vasilisa brought all she asked and went off to bed. In the night the doll built a splendid loom. By the end of the winter the linen was woven. It was so fine that you could have threaded a needle with it. In the spring they bleached the linen in the sun and Vasilisa said to the old woman, "Sell the cloth, granny, and keep the money for yourself."

The old woman looked at the linen and sighed. "No, my child. No-one but the Tsar can wear linen like this; I shall take it to the palace."

The old woman went to the royal palace and walked up and down outside the windows. The Tsar saw her and asked, "What is it you want, old woman?"

"Your Majesty," she answered, "I have brought a marvellous piece of merchandise. I do not want to show it to anyone but you."

The Tsar ordered that the old woman be let in and when he saw the linen he was amazed.

"What are you asking for it?" inquired the Tsar.

"It's beyond price, Your Majesty. I have brought it as a gift for you."

The Tsar thanked her and sent the old woman away with gifts of her own. The Tsar ordered that the material be made into shirts. They cut it out, but nowhere could they find a needlewoman willing to take on the work. After searching long and fruitlessly, the Tsar at last sent for the old woman and said, "You were able to spin and weave this linen; you can sew it into shirts."

"I was not the one who span and wove the linen," the old woman replied. "It is the work of my foster-daughter."

"Well then let her do the sewing."

The old woman went back home and told Vasilisa everything.

"I knew," Vasilisa told her, "that this work would come back to me."

She locked herself in her room and set to work. She sewed without stopping and soon a dozen shirts were ready. The old woman took the shirts to the Tsar, while Vasilisa washed, did her hair, got dressed and sat beneath the window. She sat there and waited to see what would happen.

She saw one of the Tsar's servants approaching the old woman's house.

He came in and said, "His Majesty wishes to see the great craftswoman who has made him the shirts and to reward her in person."

Vasilisa went and presented herself to the Tsar. As soon as the Tsar saw Vasilisa the Beautiful he fell deeply in love with her.

"No, my beauty," he said, "I'll not be parted from you. You shall be my wife."

At that the Tsar took Vasilisa by her lily-white hands and sat her down next to him and they had their wedding with no more ado. Soon Vasilisa's father returned. He was delighted at his daughter's good fortune and went to live in the palace as well. Vasilisa also took the old woman with her, and she kept the little doll in her pocket to the end of her days.

Snegurochka

Once upon a time there was a couple named Ivan and Maria. They lived together for a long time in harmony and loved each other. Everything would have been fine, but they had one great sorrow. They were starting to grow old and still had no children.

Winter came. One night there was a heavy fall of snow. In the morning the children poured out of their houses. They went sledging, threw snowballs and then set about making a snowman.

Ivan and Maria sat by the window and watched their neighbours' children.

Maria sighed and Ivan suddenly said, "Come on, Mariushka, let's go and make a snowman too. It's a wonderful day to be outside!"

"Yes, let's. Only we won't make a snowman, we'll shape a little child out of snow – a daughter."

And so they started to fashion a figure out of snow in their garden. They made a body, added legs and arms, and then a head. Ivan shaped the nose and made a couple of hollows for the eyes. The sun suddenly appeared from behind a cloud and the snow sparkled under Ivan's fingers as if the eyes were glistening. And when he moulded the lips they turned pink and smiled. The figure shifted its shoulders, as if shrugging; then moved its arms and legs.

"Ivan!" Maria exclaimed. "Our daughter's come to life!"

She grabbed the snow figure by the arm and dragged it into the house, repeating over and over, "My little longed-for daughter! My darling Snegúrochka!"

So Snegurochka began to live with them, growing not by the day, but by the hour. Before winter was out she was quite a big girl. Every day she grew more beautiful. Her eyes were blue; her light brown plait hung down below her waist; her face was white as snow; only her lips were bright red. She smiled all the time. Snegurochka was so affectionate, friendly and bright that all the girls in the village began gathering at Maria and Ivan's cottage. They taught Snegurochka to sew and knit and embroider. And the songs she learnt from them! Her voice was pure and clear; when she sang everyone listened spellbound.

Ivan and Maria adored their daughter. Winter passed and the spring sun began to warm the earth. Everyone was pleased, but Snegurochka grew sad. She was quieter and gloomier with every passing day. Ivan and Maria kept asking her, "What's the matter, daughter? You aren't ill, are you?"

"It's nothing, father. Don't worry, mother. I am well…"

But she hid herself from the warm sun. She took herself down to the cool stream, in the shade of the willows, and even sang a song now and again. She was happy when dark clouds covered the sky. On one occasion the sky grew black and hailstones poured down. Snegurochka was delighted, as if she had been given a little brother. But when the sun peeped out again and the hail began to melt, she cried bitterly… Nobody had ever seen tears on her face before.

Summer came around. The evenings were long and bright. One evening the village girls gathered in a birch grove to sing songs and dance. They called on Snegurochka to join them. She did not want to go and Maria was not keen to let her, but then she thought that it might cheer her daughter up.

"Go on, my child," she said to Snegurochka. "Run along with your friends. And, girls, look after our daughter. Don't upset her."

The girls took Snegurochka by the arm and ran singing to the grove. While the sun was setting, the girls danced a round dance, then picked flowers and plaited wreaths for their heads. Later when darkness fell they gathered brushwood, lit a bonfire and started to jump over it.

Snegurochka stood off to one side, watching. The girls noticed, ran up to her and began to encourage and nag her. She rejoined them. The girls jumped over the fire, laughed and shouted... But suddenly, behind them came a groan or a sigh, "Aaah!"

They looked round, but there was no-one there.

They glanced in fright at one another and someone whispered, "Girls, where's Snegurochka?"

The children dashed around, looking for Snegurochka. They spread out across the whole grove, calling her name. They looked everywhere, but couldn't find her. Indeed she was nowhere to be found.

As soon as Snegurochka had approached the fire, she was caught by the heat and carried upwards. That was when she sighed. At that moment a light haze rose above the flames, turned into a little cloud and was carried away by the wind, over the forests, over the sea...

They looked for Snegurochka the next day, and the one after. And how Ivan and Maria grieved over their daughter. They spent all their days wandering around the grove, shouting "Hey! Snegurochka! Hey! Daughter!"

People do say that the couple wander the woods and forests to this day, looking for Snegurochka.

If you go into the forest, keep your eyes open for them. Maria wears a yellow kerchief, Ivan a violet shirt. They are always together, never parted.

Khavroshechka

There are in this world good people, people who are not so bad and those who simply have no shame.

It was among this last sort that Little Khavróshechka found herself after her parents died. She was taken in by a woman who brought her up and set her to work all the hours that God sent: she wove and span as well as cleaning and tidying and being responsible for the whole household.

Now her mistress had three daughters. The eldest was called One-Eye, the second Two-Eyes and the third Three-Eyes.

Those daughters had nothing better to do than to sit by the gate and watch what happened in the street, while Little Khavroshechka did all the work for them: sewed all their clothes, span and wove for them — and never heard a kind word from anybody.

When she felt really sad, Little Khavroshechka went out into the field and threw her arms around the neck of the family's piebald cow, pressed herself to its warm side and poured out her heart:

"O dear cow. They beat and scold me, don't give me bread and tell me not to cry. By tomorrow I am supposed to spin and weave five poods of flax, bleach the linen and roll it all up."

The cow replied:

"My beautiful girl, climb into one of my ears and out of the other and everything will be done."

And that is just how it was: Khavroshechka climbed into one of the cow's ears and out of the other and everything was ready. The flax had been woven and bleached and now lay in rolls.

She carried the linen in to her mistress. The woman looked, grunted and hid it away in a chest. Then she gave Little Khavroshechka even more work to do.

Again the unfortunate girl went out to the cow, hugged and stroked it, climbed in one ear and out of the other. She gratefully took up the finished work and carried it to her mistress.

This time the woman called her daughter One-Eye and said to her:

"Good daughter, lovely daughter, go and look who is helping the orphan; who is spinning and weaving and rolling the linen."

One-Eye followed Khavroshechka into the forest and out again into the field, but it was a warm day. She forgot her mother's orders, lay down on the grass and soaked up the sun.

Khavroshechka whispered:

"Sleep, little eye. Sleep, little eye."

And One-Eye's eye dozed off. While One-Eye was asleep, the cow wove and bleached and rolled the linen. So the mistress learnt nothing and decided to send her second daughter, Two-Eyes:

"Good daughter, lovely daughter, go and look who is helping the orphan; who is spinning and weaving and rolling the linen."

Two-Eyes followed Khavroshechka, but it was a warm day. She forgot her mother's orders, lay down on the grass and soaked up the sun.

Khavroshechka whispered:

"Sleep, one little eye. Sleep, two little eyes."

And Two-Eyes' eyes dozed off. The cow wove and bleached and rolled the linen, and Two-Eyes kept on sleeping.

The old woman grew angry and on the third day she sent her youngest daughter, Three-Eyes, and gave the poor orphan even more work to do. Three-Eyes danced and skipped about, grew warm in the sun and lay down on the grass.

Khavroshechka whispered:

"Sleep, one little eye. Sleep, two little eyes."

But she forgot about the third eye. Two of Three-Eyes' eyes did doze off, but one stayed awake and watched all that happened. It saw Khavroshechka climb in one of the cow's ears and out of the other and then pick up the finished linen.

Three-Eyes went back home and told her mother all about it. The spiteful woman was delighted and the next day she began nagging her husband to slaughter the piebald cow.

The old man tried to argue with her:

"Have you gone mad? The cow is still young and a good milker."

"Slaughter it, and be quick about it!"

She would not budge and the old man began sharpening the knife.

Khavroshechka found out, ran into the field, hugged the piebald cow and said:

"Dear cow, they are going to kill you."

And the cow replied:

"Then you, my beautiful girl, should not eat my meat, but collect my bones, wrap them in a cloth, bury them in the garden and never forget me. Go out and water the bones every morning."

The old man slaughtered the cow and Khavroshechka followed the animal's instructions faithfully. Though she was tormented by hunger, she never ate its meat. She buried its bones and watered them in the garden every day.

And from the bones a wonderful apple-tree sprang up — with ripe juicy apples, golden leaves and heavy silver branches. All who rode by stopped to look, and those who came close simply stood and stared.

One day the three sisters, One-Eye, Two-Eyes and Three-Eyes, were strolling in the garden when a fine figure of a man rode by — rich, young and curly-haired. He saw the lovely juicy apples in the garden and he called out to the sisters:

"My fine young ladies, I have decided to marry whichever of you brings me one of those apples!"

The sisters rushed to be first to the tree.

The apples had been hanging low, where they were easy to reach, but now they suddenly sprang up high above the girls' heads.

The sisters tried to knock them down, but the leaves got in their eyes. They tried to pull off the branches, but the branches tied themselves in knots.

They struggled and strained, but they got nothing more than skinned hands for their pains.

Then Khavroshechka went up to the tree. The branches bowed down to her and the apples put themselves into her hands. She offered the best one to the young man and he took her away to be his wife. From that time on she lived happily and never knew any more sorrow.

 ## Finist the Bright Falcon

There was once a peasant whose wife died, leaving him with three daughters. The old man wanted to hire a housekeeper to look after the house, but Maryúsh-ka, the youngest daughter, said, "There's no need for a housekeeper, father, I will look after the house myself." And so it was agreed. Maryushka began to look after the house. She knew how to do everything and everything went well.

The father loved Maryushka and was happy that he had such a clever and hard-working daughter growing up. More than that, Maryushka was as pretty as any picture. Her sisters, though, were envious of her and mean to her. They were not beautiful, but terribly fond of fashion. They spent all their time powdering and rouging their faces, and dressing in new clothes. All they thought about were dresses, boots and shawls.

One day the father was setting off to market and asked his daughters, "What should I buy for you girls to make you happy?"

And the two older daughters said, "Buy us a kerchief each, with a pattern of big flowers worked in gold."

But Maryushka stood silent. Her father asked again, "What should I buy for you, daughter?"

"Father, buy me a feather of Fínist the Bright Falcon."

When he returned, their father brought kerchiefs for the two eldest, but he couldn't find the feather.

The time came for the father to go off to market again.

"Well, girls," he said, "order your presents."

The eldest two daughters were delighted.

"Buy us a pair of boots each with silver heels."

But Maryushka again answered, "Father, buy me a feather of Finist the Bright Falcon."

The father went round the market the whole day. He bought the boots, but he couldn't find the feather. And came home without it.

The old man went off to market a third time, and the two eldest girls said, "Buy us a dress each."

But Maryushka again said, "Father, buy me a feather of Finist the Bright Falcon."

The father spent the whole day looking, but he couldn't find the feather. As he was leaving town he met an old, old man coming the other way.

"Good evening to you, grandfather."

"Good evening to you. Whither are you bound?"

"Home to my village, grandfather. But it's with a heavy heart that I go. My youngest daughter asked me to buy a feather of Finist the Bright Falcon and I could not find one."

"I myself have such a feather. It is very dear to me, but for the sake of a good person I am willing to part with it."

The old, old man took out the feather and handed it over. There looked to be nothing special about it. The peasant rode home wondering why it was so important to Maryushka. The father brought his daughters their presents. The two eldest quickly dressed up and poked fun at Maryushka.

"You were always a fool. Stick your feather in your hair and show off!"

Maryushka kept quiet, avoided their company and then, when everyone had gone to bed, she tossed the feather on the floor and whispered, "Dear Finist the Bright Falcon, appear to me, my long-awaited suitor!"

And a young man more handsome than can be described did indeed appear to her. At dawn he struck the floor and turned into a falcon. Maryushka opened the window for him and the falcon flew up into the deep blue sky. Three times Maryushka welcomed her suitor. By day he flew as a falcon through the azure skies, but when night came he flew to Maryushka and became a fine young man. On the fourth day her wicked sisters noticed and told on her to their father.

"Dear daughters," he said, "you would do better to look to yourselves."

"Very well," the two girls thought, "let's see how things develop."

They stuck sharp knives into the window frame and then hid to watch what would happen. The Bright Falcon flew down. He came to the window, but couldn't get into Maryushka's room. He struggled and struggled, cut his breast to ribbons, but Maryushka slept on and didn't hear. And then the falcon spoke, "Whoever needs me will find me, but it won't be easy. You will find me when you have worn out three pairs of iron shoes, broken three iron staffs and torn three iron hats."

Maryushka heard this, leapt out of bed and looked out of the window, but the falcon was gone, leaving only bloody marks on the pane. Maryushka wept bitterly, washed the bloody marks away with her tears and became more beautiful than ever.

She went to her father and said, "Do not scold me, father. I must go on a long journey. If I live we shall see each other again; if I die then that is how it was meant to be."

The father felt very sorry for his favourite daughter, but he agreed that she should go. Maryushka had three pairs of iron shoes made, three iron staffs and three iron hats, and set off on her long journey to find her beloved – Finist the Bright Falcon. She walked across open steppes, through dark forests and over tall mountains. The birds sang jolly songs to gladden her heart, the streams washed her fair face and the dark woods greeted her. And nothing could harm Maryushka: grey wolves, bears, foxes – all wild creatures came running to her. She wore out a pair of iron shoes, broke an iron staff and tore an iron hat. One day Maryushka came out into a clearing and saw there a hut on chicken legs turning around.

Maryushka called out, "Hut, o hut, stand with your back to the trees, your front to me! I want to get in and eat bread."

The hut turned so its back was to the trees and its front to Maryushka. The girl climbed in and saw Baba-Yaga with the leg of bone sitting there, her legs from one corner to the other, her lips on a shelf and her nose grown into the ceiling.

Baba-Yaga caught sight of Maryushka and called out, "Pish and pah! I smell a Russian soul! Well, my pretty one, are you looking for an adventure, or looking to avoid one?"

"I am seeking Finist the Bright Falcon, grandma."

"Well, my pretty one, you'll not find him soon. Your Bright Falcon is in a land far, far away. The enchantress Tsarina gave him a potion and made him marry her. Take this silver dish and gold egg. When you come to that land far, far away, go to work for the Tsarina. When you have done your work take the dish, put the gold egg in it and it will roll of its own accord. When you are asked to sell it, refuse. Ask to see Finist the Bright Falcon."

Maryushka thanked Baba-Yaga and went on her way. The forest grew dark, Maryushka grew scared. She hesitated to take another step when a cat came towards her. He sprang towards her and purred, "Don't be afraid, Maryushka. Go on. It will get even scarier, but you keep going and don't look back."

The cat rubbed his back and was gone. Maryushka went on and the forest grew darker still. Maryushka walked and walked. She wore out a pair of iron shoes, broke an iron staff, tore an iron hat and came to a hut on chicken legs. Around it stood a fence of stakes, with a skull on each one and each skull glowed with light.

Maryushka called out, "Hut, o hut, stand with your back to the trees, your front to me! I want to get in and eat bread."

The hut turned so its back was to the trees and its front to Maryushka. The girl climbed in and saw Baba-Yaga with the leg of bone sitting there, her legs from one corner to the other, her lips on a shelf and her nose grown into the ceiling.

Baba-Yaga caught sight of Maryushka and called out, "Pish and pah! I smell a Russian soul! Well, my pretty one, are you looking for an adventure, or looking to avoid one?"

"I am seeking Finist the Bright Falcon, grandma."

"Have you seen my sister?"

"Yes, grandma."

"Very well, my pretty one, I shall help you. Take this silver embroidery hoop and gold needle. The needle will embroider of its own accord with gold and silver thread on crimson velvet. When you are asked to sell it, refuse. Ask to see Finist the Bright Falcon."

Maryushka thanked Baba-Yaga and went on her way. The forest was full of noises, cracks and whines. Skulls lit up the trees. Maryushka grew afraid. She looked and saw a dog running towards her.

"Woof, woof, Maryushka. Don't be afraid, my dear. Go on. It will get even scarier, but don't look back."

It spoke and was gone. Maryushka went on and the forest grew darker still. Roots caught her legs, branches snagged her arms. Maryushka walked and walked, and didn't look back. A long time went by, or maybe a short one, but she wore out a pair of iron shoes, broke an iron staff and tore an iron hat. She came to a clearing, and there stood a hut on chicken legs. Around it stood a fence of stakes, with a horse's skull on each one and each skull glowed with light.

Maryushka called out, "Hut, o hut, stand with your back to the trees, your front to me! I want to get in and eat bread."

The hut turned so its back was to the trees and its front to Maryushka. The girl climbed in and saw Baba-Yaga with the leg of bone sitting there, her legs from one corner to the other, her lips on a shelf and her nose grown into the ceiling.

Baba-Yaga caught sight of Maryushka and called out, "Pish and pah! I smell a Russian soul! Well, my pretty one, are you looking for an adventure, or looking to avoid one?"

"I am seeking Finist the Bright Falcon, grandma."

"You will have a hard time finding him, my pretty one, but I shall help. Take this silver distaff and gold spindle. Pick it up and it will spin of its own accord – not ordinary thread, but gold."

"Thank you, grandma."

"Thank you can wait, but listen now to what I tell you. When you are asked to sell the gold spindle, refuse. Ask to see Finist the Bright Falcon."

Maryushka thanked Baba-Yaga and went on her way. The forest cracked and howled. Owls circled round, mice came out of their holes and all made for Maryushka. The girl saw a grey wolf running towards her.

"Don't despair," he said. "Climb on me and don't look back."

Maryushka climbed onto the grey wolf and they flew like the wind. Ahead lay broad steppes, velvety meadows, rivers of honey, banks of kissel, mountains reaching up to the clouds. Maryushka rode on and on, until there appeared before her a crystal palace with a carved porch and a patterned window, and looking out of that window was the Tsarina.

"Well," said the wolf, "off you get, Maryushka. Go and get yourself hired as a servant."

Maryushka climbed off, took her bundle, thanked the wolf and went up to the crystal palace. Maryushka bowed to the Tsarina and said, "I do not know your name or title, but do you need a servant in your household?"

The Tsarina replied, "I have long been looking for a servant, but she must be able to spin, weave and embroider."

"I can do all that."

"Then come in and start work."

So Maryushka became a servant. She worked all day and when evening came Maryushka took the silver dish and gold egg and said, "Roll, roll, gold egg around the silver bowl. Show me my sweetheart."

The egg rolled around the silver bowl and Finist the Bright Falcon appeared. Maryushka looked at him and her eyes filled with tears.

"Finist, Finist, my bright falcon, why did you leave me alone, to weep bitterly over you!"

The Tsarina heard those words and said, "Maryushka, sell me the silver bowl and gold egg."

"No," said Maryushka. "They are not for sale. I can give them to you, though, if you let me look upon Finist the Bright Falcon."

The Tsarina thought long and hard.

"Very well," she said, "so be it. Tonight, when he is asleep, I shall show him to you."

Night came and Maryushka was allowed into the bedroom to see Finist the Bright Falcon. She found her beloved fast asleep. She looked and looked and could not look her fill. She kissed his sweet lips and pressed herself to his chest, but her darling slept on and did not stir. Morning came and Maryushka had failed to wake her sweetheart.

Maryushka worked all day and when evening came she took the silver embroidery hoop and gold needle. She sat over her needlework and said to herself, "Sew, sew a pattern, for Finist the Bright Falcon. Make a fine towel for him to dry himself in the mornings."

The Tsarina heard and said, "Maryushka, sell me the silver embroidery hoop and gold needle."

"I will not sell them," said Maryushka, "but I will give them to you, if you let me see Finist the Bright Falcon."

The Tsarina thought long and hard.

"Very well," she said, "so be it. Come again tonight."

Night came and Maryushka was allowed into the bedroom to see Finist the Bright Falcon, but he was fast asleep.

"Finist, my bright falcon, wake up, get up!"

Finist the Bright Falcon slept soundly. Try as she might, Maryushka could not wake him. Morning came. Maryushka sat at her work. She took up the silver distaff and gold spindle. The Tsarina saw them.

"Do sell them to me."

"I will not sell them," said Maryushka, "but I will give them to you, if you let me see Finist the Bright Falcon, if only for an hour."

"Very well," said the other, thinking to herself, "She'll never wake him anyway."

Night came and Maryushka was allowed into the bedroom to see Finist the Bright Falcon, but he was fast asleep.

"Finist, my bright falcon, wake up, get up!"

Finist the Bright Falcon slept soundly. Try as she might, Maryushka could not wake him. Dawn was approaching and Maryushka burst into tears.

"My darling Finist, my bright falcon, wake up, get up, look upon your Maryushka, press her to your heart."

One of Maryushka's tears fell on the bare shoulder of Finist the Bright Falcon and scalded him. Finist the Bright Falcon awoke, looked around and saw Maryushka. He hugged and kissed her.

"Is it really you, Maryushka. Have you worn out three pairs of iron shoes, broken three iron staffs, torn three iron hats and found me? Let's go home now."

They started to prepare for the journey, but the Tsarina noticed and gave orders to sound the trumpets and announce her husband's betrayal. The princes and merchants gathered and began to discuss how Finist the Bright Falcon should be punished. Then Finist the Bright Falcon spoke up:

"Which do you think is the real wife – the one who loves firmly or the one who sells and deceives?"

All were agreed that the true wife of Finist the Bright Falcon was Maryushka. The couple hugged and kissed and they returned to their own country. They held a feast, sounded the trumpets, fired the cannon and the feast was such a great event that people remember it to this day.

Sivka-Burka

There once was an old man who had three sons. The eldest two looked after the farm. They were quite wealthy and thought a lot of themselves, but the youngest, known as Ivan the Fool, was nothing much to look at and liked to gather mushrooms in the forest, while at home he spent most of his time sitting in the warm on the stove. The time came for the old man to die and he told his sons:

"When I have gone, you should come to my grave three nights in succession and bring me bread."

Soon they buried the old man. When night came, the eldest brother was supposed to go to the grave, but, because he was lazy or because he was afraid, he did not feel like it and said to the youngest:

"Vanya, take my place tonight. Go to father's grave and I'll buy you some spice-cake."

Ivan agreed, took some bread and went to his father's grave. There he sat and waited. At midnight the earth opened, the old man rose up out of the grave and asked:

"Who's there? Is that you, my eldest son? Tell me what is happening in Russia: are the dogs barking, the wolves howling, or my children crying?"

Ivan replied: "It is me, your son. And in Russia all is well."

The father ate his fill of bread and lay back in the grave. Ivan headed for home, gathering mushrooms on the way. When he got back, the eldest brother asked him:

"Did you see father?"

"Yes, I did."

"Did he eat the bread?"

"Yes, he ate his fill."

The second night came round. It was the middle brother's turn to go, but, because he was lazy or because he was afraid, he did not feel like it and said to the youngest:

"Vanya, go to father's grave for me and I'll make you a pair of bast shoes."

"All right."

Ivan took some bread, went to his father's grave, sat and waited. At midnight the earth opened, the old man rose up out of the grave and asked:

"Who's there? Is that you, my middle son? Tell me what is happening in Russia: are the dogs barking, the wolves howling, or my children crying?"

Ivan replied:

"It is me, your son. And in Russia all is well."

The father ate his fill of bread and lay back in the grave.

Ivan headed for home, gathering mushrooms again on the way. When he got back, the middle brother asked him:

"Did father eat the bread?"

"Yes, he ate his fill."

On the third night it was Ivan's own turn to go. He said to his brothers:

"I have been for two nights now. You go to father's grave this time and I shall have a rest."

But his brothers answered:

"No, no, Vanya. You know what it's like already, you'd better go."

"Very well then."

Ivan took some bread and went. At midnight the earth opened, the old man rose up out of the grave and asked:

"Who's there? Is it you, my youngest son? Tell me what is happening in Russia: are the dogs barking, the wolves howling, or my children crying?"

Ivan replied:

"It is me, your son, Vanya. And in Russia all is well."

The father ate his fill of bread, then held out a bridle and said to him:

"You alone have done as I asked and have not been afraid to come to my grave. Go out into the open country and shout: 'Sivka-Burka, wonder-worker, appear before me, like a leaf before a tree!' A horse will come running to you. Climb into its right ear and out of the left and you'll become a very fine young man. Get on the horse and go for a ride."

Ivan took the bridle, thanked his father and went home, gathering mushrooms again on the way. At home his brothers asked him:

"Did you see father?"

"Yes, I did."

"Did he eat the bread."

"Father ate his fill and did not ask us to come again."

Just at that time the Tsar sent word for all fine, young unmarried men to ride to his court. His daughter, the Incomparable Beauty, had given orders for a special tall tower to be built for her with a dozen columns and a dozen tiers of logs. She was going to sit at the very top of that tower and wait to see who could reach her with a single jump of his horse and kiss her on the lips. The horseman who succeeded, no matter what his birth, would receive the Tsar's daughter's hand in marriage and half the kingdom into the bargain. Ivan's brothers heard this news and said to each other:

"Come on, let's go and try our luck."

They fed their best horses with oats, brought them out, dressed up smartly, and combed their hair. Then Ivan, who was sitting on the stove behind the chimney, called out:

"Brothers, take me with you so I can try my luck."

"You stove-loving simpleton. You'd be better going into the forest for mushrooms. There's no call to make a fool of yourself in front of people."

The brothers mounted their horses, cocked their hats, whistled and whooped — then all you could see of them was a cloud of dust. Ivan took the bridle and went out into the open country. Once he was there he shouted out the words his father had taught him:

"Sivka-Burka, wonder-worker, appear before me, like a leaf before a tree!"

From out of nowhere a horse came galloping. The earth trembled; flame spurted from its nostrils and columns of smoke poured from its ears. It stopped as if rooted to the spot and asked:

"What is your command?"

Ivan stroked the horse and put the bridle on it. He climbed into its right ear and out of its left, becoming a finer fellow than can be imagined or described. He mounted the horse and rode to the Tsar's court. As Sivka-Burka ran, the earth shook beneath its hooves, mountains and valleys flew by in a trice. Ivan came to the Tsar's court and found it full of more people than you could possibly count. The Incomparable Beauty sat at the very top of the tall tower.

The Tsar came out onto the porch and announced:

"Whosoever of you fine young men shall jump on his horse up to that window and kiss my daughter on the lips shall have her hand in marriage and half the kingdom as a dowry."

Then the young fellows began to jump... but the window was so high as to be simply unreachable. Ivan's brothers had their try, and did not even get halfway up. Finally Ivan's turn came.

He urged his horse to the fore, he tore, he roared, he soared — and was only two logs short of the window. He turned around and took off again — just one log short. Again he turned, circled, fired up his steed and away — he flew like a bird past the window. He kissed the princess on her lovely lips and she struck him on the forehead with her ring, leaving her mark on him.

The whole crowd erupted: "Hold him! Stop him!"

But Ivan was already long gone. He rode out into the open country, climbed into Sivka-Burka's left ear and out of his right, again becoming Ivan the Fool. He let the horse go and made his way home on foot, gathering mushrooms as he went. He wrapped a cloth around his forehead, climbed onto the stove and lay down. His brothers came back and told him where they had been and what they had seen.

"There were fine fellows there, but one better than all the rest — flew up on his horse and kissed the princess on the lips. People saw where he came from, but no-one saw where he went."

Ivan perched behind the chimney and said:

"Well, perhaps it was me."

His brothers became angry with him:

"The fool's talking nonsense! Sit on the stove and eat your mushrooms."

Ivan quietly unwrapped the cloth over his forehead where the princess had struck him with her ring. The room filled with light. His brothers took fright and shouted:

"Hey, you fool, what are you doing? You'll set the house on fire!"

The next day the Tsar summoned everyone to a feast, all the boyars and princes, and the common people too, rich and poor, old and young. Ivan's brothers began getting ready for the feast. Ivan asked them to take him with them, but they replied:

"Why do you want to make a fool of yourself in public? Sit on the stove and eat your mushrooms!"

The brothers mounted their best horses and rode off; Ivan followed on foot. He came to the Tsar's feast and took a seat in a far corner. Princess Incomparable Beauty began to go around all the guests. She carried round a bowl of mead while looking out for someone with the mark on his forehead.

She had been to everyone by the time she reached Ivan. And suddenly her heart skipped. She looked at him, covered in soot with his hair uncombed. The Princess began questioning him:

"Whose man are you? Where are you from? Why is your forehead bandaged?"

"I hurt myself."

The Princess unbandaged his forehead and suddenly light filled the palace. She cried out:

"That's my mark! Here's my future husband!"

The Tsar came up and said:

"What future husband! He's ugly and covered in soot."

Ivan said to the Tsar:

"Allow me to clean myself up."

The Tsar agreed. Ivan went out into the courtyard and shouted out the words his father had taught him:

"Sivka-Burka, wonder-worker, appear before me, like a leaf before a tree!"

From out of nowhere a horse came galloping. The earth trembled; flame spurted from its nostrils and columns of smoke poured from its ears. He climbed into its right ear and out of its left, again becoming a finer fellow than can be imagined or described. The entire crowd gasped.

After that, the discussions did not last long and the happy gathering turned into a wedding feast.

The Fire-Bird
and Princess Vasilisa

Once upon a time in a country far, far away, there lived a great and powerful tsar. Now that tsar had a very fine archer and that archer had a most noble steed. One day the archer rode out into the forest on his most noble steed to go hunting. As he was riding down the broad track he came upon a golden feather from the Fire-Bird, all aglow like a flame!

His most noble steed spoke to him, "Don't take the golden feather. If you do, there's trouble ahead."

And the fine young fellow began wondering whether to pick up the feather or not. If he took it and presented it to the tsar, he would be richly rewarded and to be in a ruler's favour is always a good thing. The archer disregarded his horse's advice, picked up the Fire-Bird's feather and presented it to the tsar.

"My thanks," said the tsar. "And since you have brought a feather from the Fire-Bird, bring me the bird itself. And should you fail to do so, my axe will give your neck some whacks!"

The archer burst into bitter tears and went to see his most noble steed.

"Why are you crying, master?"

"The tsar has ordered me to fetch the Fire-Bird."

"Didn't I tell you that if you took the feather there was trouble ahead? Well, don't worry, that is no trouble; the trouble is yet to come! Go back to the tsar and ask that a hundred sacks of the finest grain be scattered across all the open field by tomorrow."

The tsar gave orders for a hundred sacks of the finest grain be scattered across all the open field. At dawn the next day the very fine archer rode out into the field. He left his horse to wander and himself hid behind a tree.

Suddenly the forest stirred, the waves rose on the sea – the Fire-Bird was coming. It flew down, alighted on the ground and started pecking at the grain. The most noble steed walked up to the Fire-Bird, put his hoof on its wing and held it firmly to the ground. The very fine archer jumped out from behind the tree, ran up and bound the Fire-Bird with rope. He mounted his horse and galloped to the palace.

He brought the Fire-Bird to the tsar. The tsar was delighted at the sight of it, thanked the archer for his services and granted him a high rank. But straightaway he gave him another task.

"Since you managed to bring me the Fire-Bird, bring me a bride. Far, far away, at the end of the world, where the red sun rises, lives Princess Vasilisa. She is the one I must have. If you bring her, gold and silver will be your reward. Should you fail to do so, my axe will give your neck some whacks!"

The archer burst into bitter tears and went to see his most noble steed.

"Why are you crying, master?"

"The tsar has ordered me to fetch Princess Vasilisa."

"Don't cry, don't despair. That is no trouble; the trouble is yet to come! Go back to the tsar, ask for a tent with a golden top and fine food and drink for the journey."

The tsar gave him food and drink, and a tent with a golden top. The very fine archer mounted his most noble steed and set off on his journey.

After a long time, or maybe a short one, he came to the end of the world, where the red sun rises from the deep blue sea. He looked and there he saw Princess Vasilisa out on the blue sea, rowing a silver boat with a golden oar.

The very fine archer left his horse to wander in the lush meadows and crop the green grass. Meanwhile he put up the tent with the golden top, laid a table with fine food and drink and sat down to enjoy a meal and wait for Princess Vasilisa.

Princess Vasilisa caught sight of the gold-topped tent, rowed into the shore, climbed out of her boat and came up to admire it.

"Greetings, Princess Vasilisa," the very fine archer called out. "Come in and enjoy our hospitality, try some foreign wines."

Princess Vasilisa went into the tent. She began to eat and drink and enjoy herself. The princess drank a glass of foreign wine that went to her head and she fell into a deep sleep. The very fine archer called for his most noble steed. The horse ran up. The archer immediately packed up the gold-topped tent. He mounted his most noble steed, putting the sleeping Princess Vasilisa before him and rode off like the wind.

He came back to the tsar. The tsar was delighted at the sight of Princess Vasilisa. He thanked the archer for his services, gave him a great reward and granted him an even higher rank. Princess Vasilisa awoke, found that she was far, far from the deep blue sea and began to cry and pine so much she lost her beauty. However much the tsar tried to wheedle her, nothing changed.

The tsar was still determined to marry her, but she said, "Let the one who brought me here go to the deep blue sea. In the middle of that sea lies a great stone and hidden beneath that stone is my wedding dress. Without that dress I will not marry."

The tsar immediately sent for his very fine archer.

"Go at once to the end of the world, where the red sun rises. There, in the deep blue sea, lies a great stone and hidden beneath that stone is Princess Vasilisa's wedding dress. Find the dress and bring it here. The time has come to wed! If you bring it, I shall give you a reward greater than before. Should you fail to do so, my axe will give your neck some whacks!"

The archer burst into bitter tears and went to see his most noble steed.

"Why are you crying, master?"

"The tsar has ordered me to fetch Princess Vasilisa's wedding dress from the bottom of the sea."

"Didn't I tell you that if you took the feather there was trouble ahead? Well, don't worry, that is no trouble; the trouble is yet to come! Get into the saddle and let's go to the deep blue sea."

After a long time, or maybe a short one, the very fine archer came to the end of the world, and stopped by the deep blue sea. The most noble steed spotted a huge lobster crawling over the sand and planted his heavy hoof on its tail. The lobster called out, "Do not kill me, let me live! I shall do whatever you ask!"

The horse replied, "In the middle of the deep blue sea lies a great stone, and hidden beneath that stone is Princess Vasilisa's wedding dress. Get us that dress!"

The lobster called out in a loud voice to the whole of the deep blue sea. Immediately the sea stirred and from all sides lobsters big and small began crawling out onto the shore in great numbers. The oldest lobster gave them orders. They plunged back into the sea and within the hour they had fetched Princess Vasilisa's wedding dress from under the great stone at the bottom of the sea. The very fine archer returned to the tsar, bringing the wedding dress. But Princess Vasilisa again proved stubborn.

"I will not marry you," she told the tsar, "until you command the very fine archer to bathe in boiling water."

The tsar ordered that a great iron cauldron be filled with water and heated to boiling and that the archer then be thrown into it. They did as he said. The water boiled, bubbling and spitting, and they brought in the poor archer.

"Now the trouble has come," he thought.

"Why did I pick up the Fire-Bird's golden feather? Why didn't I listen to my horse?"

He remembered his most noble steed and said to the tsar, "Your Majesty, allow me to bid farewell to my horse before I die."

"Very well, do so if you must."

The archer crying bitter tears went to see his most noble steed.

"Why are you crying, master?"

"The tsar has ordered me to be plunged into boiling water."

"Don't cry, don't be afraid. You will live!" the horse told him and quickly cast a spell over the archer so that the boiling water would not harm him.

As soon as the archer returned from the stable, he was seized by servants who tossed him straight into the cauldron. He plunged in over his head once, then a second time, and sprang out of the pot more handsome than can be imagined or described. After seeing the result, the tsar wanted to get into the cauldron himself. He foolishly climbed in and was immediately scalded to death.

They buried the tsar and in his place they chose the very fine archer. He married Princess Vasilisa and they lived a long life together in love and harmony.